Test Masters
for
ELEMENTARY
ALGEBRA

Test Masters
for
ELEMENTARY
ALGEBRA

Harold R. Jacobs

W. H. FREEMAN AND COMPANY

New York

The cover illustration is a periodic drawing by Maurits Escher. Reproduced with the permission of the Escher Foundation, Haags Gemeentemuseum, The Hague.

ISBN-13: 978-0-7167-1077-6
ISBN-10: 0-7167-1077-3

Printed in the United States of America

Fifteenth printing

W. H. Freeman and Company
41 Madison Avenue
New York, NY 10010
www.whfreeman.com

Contents

Introductory Comments

This book contains chapter tests, a midyear examination, and a final examination that can be used with Elementary Algebra. The pages are perforated so that they can be removed and used to make duplicating masters with a thermographic reproduction machine. There are four versions, identified by the letters A, B, C, and D in the lower right-hand corner of each page, of each chapter test. The midyear and final examinations consist of eighty problems each; both are four pages long, with twenty problems on each page. The pages can be arranged in the orders shown below to produce four forms of the examination. Because problem 1 on one form is the same as problems 21, 41, and 61 on the other forms, and so forth, only the last digit of the number of each problem is given.

Problems	Form A	Form B	Form C	Form D
1-20	Page A	Page B	Page C	Page D
21-40	Page B	Page D	Page A	Page C
41-60	Page C	Page A	Page D	Page B
61-80	Page D	Page C	Page B	Page A

The chapter tests are designed for an examination period of approximately 45 minutes; the midyear and final are designed for an examination period of approximately 110 minutes. Complete answers for all of the tests are in a separate section at the end of this book.

Supplementary word problems and additional exercises are included in this book for duplication by those teachers who may want to use them. I selected the word problems from those found in First Lessons in Algebra by Ebenezer Bailey, published in Boston by Jenks and Palmer in 1842. The types of problems are the same as those in modern books, but their old-fashioned peculiarities add interest for students. Sets 1 and 2 are appropriate for use with chapter 5, set 3 with chapter 7, set 4 with chapter 13, and set 5 with chapter 15.

ELEMENTARY
ALGEBRA
CHAPTER TESTS

ELEMENTARY ALGEBRA
Test on Chapter 1

Name _____

Write another expression equivalent to each of the following.

1. $x + x + x$

2. $7 \cdot 7 \cdot 7 \cdot 7$

3. y^2

If possible, express each of the following as a power of the number given.

4. $10,000,000$ as a power of 10.

5. 4 as a power of 1.

6. $32,768$ as a power of 8.

The following problems are about division and zero.

7. Does it make sense to divide 0 by 15?

8. Explain why or why not.

The perimeter of a rectangle is the sum of the lengths of its sides. The area of a rectangle is the product of its length and width. What are the perimeter and area of each of these rectangles?

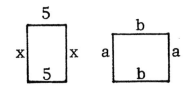

9. Perimeter of first rectangle.

10. Area of first rectangle.

11. Perimeter of second rectangle.

12. Area of second rectangle.

Write an expression for each of the following.

13. The number x multiplied by 6.

14. The difference between 2 and y.

15. The fourth power of z.

Which figure below illustrates each of these expressions?

16. $2 \cdot 3^2$

17. $2 + 3^2$

18. $(2 + 3)^2$

```
              O O  O O O
       O O O  O O  O O O   O O O  O O O
O O    O O O  O O  O O O   O O O  O O O
       O O O  O O  O O O   O O O  O O O
              O O  O O O
  Figure 1      Figure 2      Figure 3
```

Max and Minnie are taking a test.

19. If Max's score is 2 more than the average score, x, how many questions did he answer correctly?

20. If there are y questions and Minnie answers 20 of them correctly, how many did she get wrong?

Write an expression for each of the following sets of operations.

21. Multiply 5 by 7 and then cube the result.

22. Subtract 4 from 12 and then multiply by 6.

Here are directions for a number trick. Show how the trick works by drawing boxes and circles to illustrate the steps.

23. Think of a number.

24. Add three.

25. Multiply by four.

26. Subtract eight.

27. Divide by four.

28. Subtract the number that you first thought of.

29. What is the result at the end of the trick?

1A1

Write each of these products as a sum or difference.

30. $4(a + 8)$

31. $(c - d)c$

Stock of the Flim Flam Company sells for $1000 a share.

32. How many shares could be bought for y dollars?

33. How much would x shares of the stock cost?

Find the value of each of these expressions.

34. $18 + 2 \cdot 8$

35. $7 \cdot 3^2$

36. $8^2 - 2^2$

37. $30 - (12 \div 7)$

Each of the following expressions contains two unknown numbers, x and y. Simplify each expression as much as you can. Assume that neither x nor y is zero.

38. $0x + 1y$

39. $\dfrac{x}{1} - \dfrac{y}{1}$

A molecule of ammonia gas consists of one nitrogen atom and three hydrogen atoms.

40. How many of each atom do x molecules of ammonia contain?

41. Write the total number of atoms in x molecules of the gas as a sum.

42. How many atoms does one molecule of ammonia gas contain?

43. Write the total number of atoms in x molecules of the gas as a product.

Find the values of each of the following powers.

44. 5^3

45. 5^4

46. 5^5

47. Do you think the 20th power of 5 is <u>odd</u> or <u>even</u>?

Find the value of $x^2 + 20 - 9x$ if

48. x is 1

49. x is 2

50. x is 3

Extra Credit.

What symbols of operation can be used to replace the blanks in the expression

1 ||| 2 ||| 3 ||| 4 ||| 5 ||| 6 ||| 7 ||| 8 ||| 9

to make it equal to 100?

ELEMENTARY ALGEBRA
Test on Chapter 1

Name _____

Write an expression for each of the following.

1. The difference between 5 and x.

2. The number y cubed.

3. The product of z and 9.

Find the value of each of these expressions.

4. $5 \cdot 4^2$

5. $40 - (13 - 4)$

6. $14 + 2 \cdot 5$

7. $6^2 - 3^2$

Here are directions for a number trick. Show how the trick works by drawing boxes and circles to illustrate the steps.

8. Think of a number.

9. Multiply by three.

10. Add nine.

11. Divide by three.

12. Add one.

13. Subtract the number that you first thought of.

14. What is the result at the end of the trick?

If possible, express each of the following as a power of the number given.

15. 100,000 as a power of 10.

16. 14,641 as a power of 11.

17. 5 as a power of 1.

Write an expression for each of the following sets of operations.

18. Add 15 to 3 and then multiply by 4.

19. Multiply 6 by 4 and then square the result.

The following problems are about division and zero.

20. Does it make sense to divide 10 by 0?

21. Explain why or why not.

Write each of these products as a sum or difference.

22. $6(7 + a)$

23. $(c - d)d$

Each of the following expressions contains two unknown numbers, x and y. Simplify each expression as much as you can. Assume that neither x nor y is zero.

24. $1x - 0y$

25. $\dfrac{0}{x} + \dfrac{0}{y}$

Which figure below illustrates each of these expressions?

26. $3 \cdot 2^2$

27. $3^2 + 2^2$

28. $(3 + 2)^2$

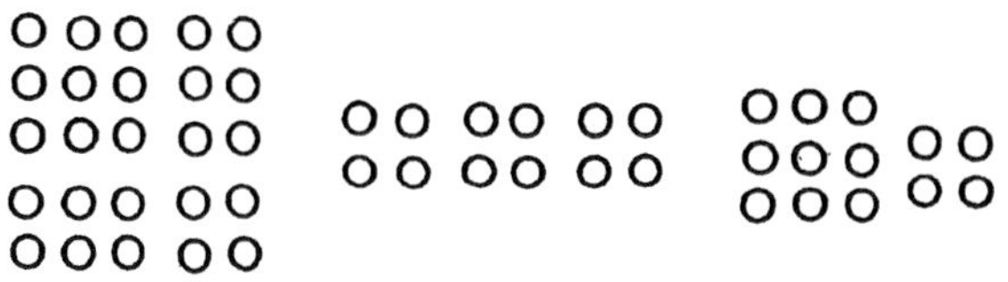

Figure 1   Figure 2   Figure 3

Max and Minnie are taking a test.

29. If there are x questions and Max answers 20 of them correctly, how many did he get wrong?

30. If Minnie's score is 2 more than the average score, y, how many did she get right?

Find the values of each of the following powers.

31. 3^5

32. 3^6

33. 3^7

34. Do you think the 20th power of 3 is <u>odd</u> or <u>even</u>?

The perimeter of a rectangle is the sum of the lengths of its sides. The area of a rectangle is the product of its length and width. What are the perimeter and area of each of these rectangles?

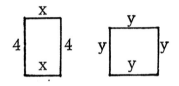

35. Perimeter of first rectangle.

36. Area of first rectangle.

37. Perimeter of second rectangle.

38. Area of second rectangle.

Write another expression equivalent to each of the following.

39. $3x$

40. $8 + 8$

41. $2 \cdot 2 \cdot 2 \cdot 2 \cdot 2$

Stock of the Flim Flam Company sells for $1000 a share.

42. How much would y shares of the stock cost?

43. How many shares could be bought for x dollars?

Find the value of $x^2 + 16 - 8x$ if

44. x is 1

45. x is 2

46. x is 3

A molecule of carbon dioxide gas consists of one carbon atom and two oxygen atoms.

47. How many of each atom do x molecules of carbon dioxide contain?

48. Write the total number of atoms in x molecules of the gas as a sum.

49. How many atoms does one carbon dioxide molecule contain?

50. Write the total number of atoms in x molecules of the gas as a product.

Extra Credit.

What symbols of operation can be used to replace the blanks in the expression

1 ||| 2 ||| 3 ||| 4 ||| 5 ||| 6 ||| 7 ||| 8 ||| 9

to make it equal to 100?

ELEMENTARY ALGEBRA
Test on Chapter 1

Name _____

Which figure below illustrates each of these expressions?

1. $4^2 + 2^2$

2. $4 \cdot 2^2$

3. $(4 + 2)^2$

Figure 1   Figure 2   Figure 3

Each of the following expressions contains two unknown numbers, x and y. Simplify each expression as much as you can. Assume that neither x nor y is zero.

4. $1x + 1y$

5. $\dfrac{x}{1} - \dfrac{0}{y}$

Stock of the Flim Flam Company sells for $1000 a share.

6. How much would x shares of the stock cost?

7. How many shares could be bought for y dollars?

Write an expression for each of the following.

8. The product of x and 5.

9. The number y squared.

10. The number z taken away from 1.

Find the value of each of these expressions.

11. $50 - (11 - 2)$

12. $16 + 2 \cdot 4$

13. $4 \cdot 5^2$

14. $7^2 - 4^2$

Write each of these products as a sum or difference.

15. $5(9 + a)$

16. $(x - y)y$

Max and Minnie are taking a test.

17. If there are 20 questions and Max answers x of them correctly, how many did he get wrong?

18. If Minnie's score is 2 less than the average score, y, how many did she get right?

The perimeter of a rectangle is the sum of the lengths of its sides. The area of a rectangle is the product of its length and width. What are the perimeter and area of each of these rectangles?

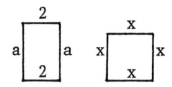

19. Perimeter of first rectangle.

20. Area of first rectangle.

21. Perimeter of second rectangle.

22. Area of second rectangle.

If possible, express each of the following as a power of the number given.

23. 10,000 as a power of 10.

24. 6 as a power of 1.

25. 6,561 as a power of 9.

The following problems are about division and zero.

26. Does it make sense to divide 20 by 0?

27. Explain why or why not.

Write another expression equivalent to each of the following.

28. $5 + 5 + 5$

29. $3 \cdot 3 \cdot 3 \cdot 3$

30. $2x$

Here are directions for a number trick. Show how the trick works by drawing boxes and circles to illustrate the steps.

31. Think of a number.

32. Add four.

33. Multiply by three.

34. Subtract nine.

35. Divide by three.

36. Subtract the number that you first thought of.

37. What is the result at the end of the trick?

Write an expression for each of the following sets of operations.

38. Cube 2 and then subtract the result from 24.

39. Add 5 to 7 and then multiply by 3.

Find the values of each of the following powers.

40. 6^3

41. 6^4

42. 6^5

43. Do you think the 15th power of 6 is <u>odd</u> or <u>even</u>?

Find the value of $x^2 + 25 - 10x$ if

44. x is 1

45. x is 2

46. x is 3

A molecule of methane gas consists of one carbon atom and four hydrogen atoms.

47. How many of each atom do x molecules of methane contain?

48. Write the total number of atoms in x molecules of the gas as a sum.

49. How many atoms does one molecule of methane gas contain?

50. Write the total number of atoms in x molecules of the gas as a product.

Extra Credit.

What symbols of operation can be used to replace the blanks in the expression

1 ▓ 2 ▓ 3 ▓ 4 ▓ 5 ▓ 6 ▓ 7 ▓ 8 ▓ 9

to make it equal to 100?

ELEMENTARY ALGEBRA
Test on Chapter 1

Name _____

Write an expression for each of the following sets of operations.

1. Add 8 to 1 and then multiply by 2.

2. Square 6 and then subtract the result from 40.

Max and Minnie are taking a test.

3. If Max's score is 2 less than the average score, x, how many questions did he answer correctly?

4. If there are 20 questions and Minnie answers y of them correctly, how many did she get wrong?

Write another expression equivalent to each of the following.

5. $8 \cdot 8 \cdot 8 \cdot 8 \cdot 8$

6. $y + y + y$

7. x^6

Write each of these products as a sum or difference.

8. $3(a + 7)$

9. $(x - y)x$

Each of the following expressions contains two unknown numbers, x and y. Simplify each expression as much as you can. Assume that neither x nor y is zero.

10. $0x - 0y$

11. $\dfrac{0}{x} + \dfrac{y}{1}$

Stock of the Flim Flam Company sells for $1000 a share.

12. How many shares could be bought for x dollars?

13. How much would y shares of the stock cost?

Here are directions for a number trick. Show how the trick works by drawing boxes and circles to illustrate the steps.

14. Think of a number.

15. Multiply by two.

16. Add ten.

17. Divide by two.

18. Add one.

19. Subtract the number that you first thought of.

20. What is the result at the end of the trick?

Write an expression for each of the following.

21. The quotient of 2 and x.

22. The number y taken away from 9.

23. The number z cubed.

The perimeter of a rectangle is the sum of the lengths of its sides. The area of a rectangle is the product of its length and width. What are the perimeter and area of each of these rectangles?

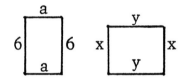

24. Perimeter of first rectangle.

25. Area of first rectangle.

26. Perimeter of second rectangle.

27. Area of second rectangle.

Find the value of each of these expressions.

28. $5^2 - 4^2$

29. $3 \cdot 7^2$

30. $60 - (15 - 8)$

31. $12 + 2 \cdot 9$

Which figure below illustrates each of the following expressions?

32. $2 + 4^2$

33. $(2 + 4)^2$

34. $2 \cdot 4^2$

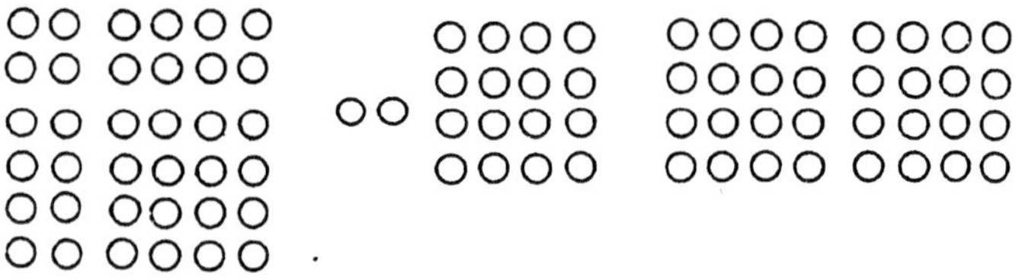

Figure 1   Figure 2   Figure 3

If possible, express each of the following as a power of the number given.

35. 100,000,000 as a power of 10.

36. 20,736 as a power of 12.

37. 3 as a power of 1.

The following problems are about division and zero.

38. Does it make sense to divide 0 by 25?

39. Explain why or why not.

Find the value of $x^2 + 30 - 11x$ if

40. x is 1

41. x is 2

42. x is 3

A molecule of nitrous oxide gas consists of two nitrogen atoms and one oxygen atom.

43. How many of each atom do x molecules of nitrous oxide contain?

44. Write the total number of atoms in x molecules of the gas as a sum.

45. How many atoms does one nitrous oxide molecule contain?

46. Write the total number of atoms in x molecules of the gas as a product.

Find the values of each of the following powers.

47. 4^4

48. 4^5

49. 4^6

50. Do you think the 15th power of 4 is odd or even?

Extra Credit.

What symbols of operation can be used to replace the blanks in the expression

1 ▯ 2 ▯ 3 ▯ 4 ▯ 5 ▯ 6 ▯ 7 ▯ 8 ▯ 9

to make it equal to 100?

1D2

ELEMENTARY ALGEBRA
Test on Chapter 2

Name _____

1. Draw a pair of axes extending 8 units in each direction from the origin. Connect the points in the following list with straight line segments in the order given to form a trapezoid.

   (1, 0) (5, 2) (2, 5) (0, 4) (1, 0)

Copy and complete the tables for the following functions.

2. Formula: $y = 3x - 1$

   Table:

x	1	2	3	4	5
y	IIII	IIII	IIII	IIII	IIII

3. Formula: $y = x^2 + 2x$

   Table:

x	0	1	2	3	4
y	IIII	IIII	IIII	IIII	IIII

4. Formula: $y = x(x - 5)$

   Table:

x	5	6	7	8	9
y	IIII	IIII	IIII	IIII	IIII

Read the following statements carefully and tell whether each is true or false.

5. The graph of every direct variation is a straight line.
6. Every point on a coordinate graph is located by a pair of numbers.
7. In an inverse variation, if one variable is doubled, then so is the other.
8. Some functions do not have formulas.

Guess a formula for the function represented by each of these tables. Begin each formula with $y =$.

9.
x	0	1	2	3	4
y	0	1	4	9	16

10.
x	1	2	3	4	5
y	8	7	6	5	4

11.
x	0	2	4	6	8
y	0	1	2	3	4

12.
x	0	1	2	3	4
y	2	7	12	17	22

Make a table of numbers for each of these functions, letting x equal 1, 2, 3, and 4, and graph each one.

13. $y = x + 4$

14. $y = 10 - 2x$

15. $y = \dfrac{6}{x}$

The time that it takes Kermit to drive to Hollywood is a function of the speed at which he drives. Here is a table for this function.

x, speed in mph	30	50	75
y, time in hours	5	3	2

16. Write a formula for this function.
17. How many miles is the trip?
18. How does the time vary with respect to the speed?
19. If this function were graphed, what would the graph look like?

The height that a ball bounces is a function of the height from which it is dropped. A typical formula for this function is $y = 0.8x$ in which x represents the height from which the ball is dropped and y represents the height of the bounce.

20. Copy and complete the following table for this function.

x	20	30	40	50	60
y	IIII	IIII	IIII	IIII	IIII

21. What type of function is this?
22. If this function were graphed, what would the graph look like?

Extra Credit.

Guess a formula for the function represented by each of these tables. Begin each formula with $y =$.

1.
x	0	1	2	3	4
y	0	3	12	27	48

2.
x	0	1	2	3	4
y	16	13	10	7	4

ELEMENTARY ALGEBRA
Test on Chapter 2

Name _____

1. Draw a pair of axes extending 8 units in each direction from the origin. Connect the points in the following list with straight line segments in the order given to form a kite.

(1, 0) (4, 1) (4, 6) (0, 3) (1, 0)

Copy and complete the tables for the following functions.

2. Formula: 2x - 3

Table: x	2	3	4	5	6
y	IIII	IIII	IIII	IIII	IIII

3. Formula: $y = x^3 + 2$

Table: x	0	1	2	3	4
y	IIII	IIII	IIII	IIII	IIII

4. Formula: $y = x(x + 4)$

Table: x	0	1	2	3	4
y	IIII	IIII	IIII	IIII	IIII

Read the following statements carefully and tell whether each is true or false.

5. If a point lies on one of the axes, one of its coordinates is zero.
6. All direct variations are linear functions.
7. The graph of every inverse variation is a curved line.
8. All functions have formulas.

Guess a formula for the function represented by each of these tables. Begin each formula with y =.

9.
x	0	3	6	9	12
y	0	1	2	3	4

10.
x	0	1	2	3	4
y	0	1	4	9	16

11.
x	1	2	3	4	5
y	6	5	4	3	2

12.
x	0	1	2	3	4
y	1	5	9	13	17

Make a table of numbers for each of these functions, letting x equal 1, 2, 3, and 4, and graph each one.

13. $y = x + 3$

14. $y = \dfrac{4}{x}$

15. $y = 8 - 2x$

The time that it takes Kermit to drive to Hollywood is a function of the speed at which he drives. Here is a table for this function.

x, speed in mph	30	60	80
y, time in hours	8	4	3

16. Write a formula for this function.
17. How many miles is the trip?
18. How does the time vary with respect to the speed?
19. If this function were graphed, what would the graph look like?

The height that a ball bounces is a function of the height from which it is dropped. A typical formula for this function is $y = 0.7x$ in which x represents the height from which the ball is dropped and y represents the height of the bounce.

20. Copy and complete the following table for this function.

x	20	30	40	50	60
y	IIII	IIII	IIII	IIII	IIII

21. What type of function is this?
22. If this function were graphed, what would the graph look like?

Extra Credit.

Guess a formula for the function represented by each of these tables. Begin each formula with y =.

1.
x	0	1	2	3	4
y	0	5	20	45	80

2.
x	0	1	2	3	4
y	14	11	8	5	2

2B

ELEMENTARY ALGEBRA
Test on Chapter 2

Name _____

1. Draw a pair of axes extending 8 units in each direction from the origin. Connect the points in the following list with straight line segments in the order given to form a rectangle.

    (6, 0)   (7, 3)   (1, 5)   (0, 2)   (6, 0)

Copy and complete the tables for the following functions.

2. Formula: $y = 4x - 1$

    Table:
x	1	2	3	4	5
y	‖‖	‖‖	‖‖	‖‖	‖‖

3. Formula: $y = x^2 + 3x$

    Table:
x	0	1	2	3	4
y	‖‖	‖‖	‖‖	‖‖	‖‖

4. Formula: $y = x(x - 2)$

    Table:
x	2	3	4	5	6
y	‖‖	‖‖	‖‖	‖‖	‖‖

Read the following statements carefully and tell whether each is true or false.

5. The constant of variation for the function $y = x$ is 0.
6. The graph of every linear function intersects the origin.
7. Some functions do not have formulas.
8. In a direct variation, if one variable is tripled, then so is the other.

Guess a formula for the function represented by each of these tables. Begin each formula with y =.

9.
x	0	1	2	3	4
y	5	7	9	11	13

10.
x	0	4	8	12	16
y	0	1	2	3	4

11.
x	0	1	2	3	4
y	0	1	8	27	64

12.
x	1	2	3	4	5
y	5	4	3	2	1

Make a table of numbers for each of these functions, letting x equal 1, 2, 3, and 4, and graph each one.

13. $y = x + 5$

14. $y = 9 - 2x$

15. $y = \dfrac{8}{x}$

The height that a ball bounces is a function of the height from which it is dropped. A typical formula for this function is $y = 0.6x$ in which x represents the height from which the ball is dropped and y represents the height of the bounce.

16. Copy and complete the following table for this function.

x	20	30	40	50	60
y	‖‖	‖‖	‖‖	‖‖	‖‖

17. What type of function is this?
18. If this function were graphed, what would the graph look like?

The time that it takes Kermit to drive to Hollywood is a function of the speed at which he drives. Here is a table for this function.

x, speed in mph	50	60	75
y, time in hours	6	5	4

19. Write a formula for this function.
20. How many miles is the trip?
21. How does the time vary with respect to the speed?
22. If this function were graphed, what would the graph look like?

Extra Credit.

Guess a formula for the function represented by each of these tables. Begin each formula with y =.

1.
x	0	1	2	3	4
y	0	2	16	54	128

2.
x	0	1	2	3	4
y	15	13	11	9	7

ELEMENTARY ALGEBRA
Test on Chapter 2

Name _____

1. Draw a pair of axes extending 8 units in each direction from the origin. Connect the points in the following list with straight line segments in the order given to form a parallelogram.

   (2, 0) (6, 2) (4, 5) (0, 3) (2, 0)

Copy and complete the tables for the following functions.

2. Formula: $y = 3x - 2$

   Table:

x	1	2	3	4	5
y	IIII	IIII	IIII	IIII	IIII

3. Formula: $y = x^3 + 1$

   Table:

x	0	1	2	3	4
y	IIII	IIII	IIII	IIII	IIII

4. Formula: $y = x(x + 5)$

   Table:

x	0	1	2	3	4
y	IIII	IIII	IIII	IIII	IIII

Read the following statements carefully and tell whether each is true or false.

5. The graph of every linear function intersects the origin.
6. All functions have formulas.
7. If the graph of a function is a curved line, it is an inverse variation.
8. The constant of variation for the function $y = x$ is 1.

Guess a formula for the function represented by each of these tables. Begin each formula with y =.

9.
x	1	2	3	4	5
y	9	8	7	6	5

10.
x	0	1	2	3	4
y	0	1	8	27	64

11.
x	0	1	2	3	4
y	1	7	13	19	25

12.
x	0	5	10	15	20
y	0	1	2	3	4

Make a table of numbers for each of these functions, letting x equal 1, 2, 3, and 4, and graph each one.

13. $y = x + 2$

14. $y = \dfrac{6}{x}$

15. $y = 12 - 3x$

The height that a ball bounces is a function of the height from which it is dropped. A typical formula for this function is $y = 0.9x$ in which x represents the height from which the ball is dropped and y represents the height of the bounce.

16. Copy and complete the following table for this function.

x	20	30	40	50	60
y	IIII	IIII	IIII	IIII	IIII

17. What type of function is this?
18. If this function were graphed, what would the graph look like?

The time that it takes Kermit to drive to Hollywood is a function of the speed at which he drives. Here is a table for this function.

x, speed in mph	30	60	90
y, time in hours	6	3	2

19. Write a formula for this function.
20. How many miles is the trip?
21. How does the time vary with respect to the speed?
22. If this function were graphed, what would the graph look like?

Extra Credit.

Guess a formula for the function represented by each of these tables. Begin each formula with y =.

1.
x	0	1	2	3	4
y	0	6	24	54	96

2.
x	0	1	2	3	4
y	13	11	9	7	5

2D

ELEMENTARY ALGEBRA
Test on Chapter 3

Name _____

Read the following statements carefully and tell whether each is true or false.

1. The opposite of a number may be larger than the number.
2. If both coordinates of a point are negative, the point is in the fourth quadrant.
3. The product of two negative numbers is always positive.
4. The sum of a number and its opposite is zero.

Find each of the following.

5. The difference between 18 and -6.
6. The product of -24 and -4.
7. The sum of -12 and 3.
8. The quotient of 20 and -2.

Write each of the following statements in symbols, letting x represent the number.

9. A certain number is more than negative two.
10. The square of a certain number is less than half the number.
11. The difference between a certain number and three is equal to five.

Here are directions for a number trick and part of a table to show what happens if the trick is done with two different numbers.

Think of a number:	1	-7
Subtract five:	|||||	|||||
Multiply by two:	|||||	|||||
Add six:	|||||	|||||
Divide by two:	|||||	|||||
Subtract the number that you first thought of:	|||||	|||||

12. Copy and complete the table.
13. Show how the trick works by illustrating the steps with boxes and circles. (Draw solid circles to represent negative numbers.)

What number should replace |||| in each of the following equations to make it true?

14. $-3(||||) = 6$
15. $|||| + 7 = -8$
16. $\dfrac{||||}{2} = -10$
17. $|||| - 9 = -1$
18. $-11 + |||| = 0$

Which of these symbols, >, =, or <, should replace |||| in each of the following?

19. $-13 - 12 \;||||\; -13(12)$
20. $(-45)^3 \;||||\; (-45)^2$
21. $19 - -75 \;||||\; 19 + 75$
22. $-8 + -8 + -8 \;||||\; -8(-8)(-8)$

Use a number line to find each of the following.

23. The number of the point midway between -3 and 7.
24. The distance between -7 and 4.
25. The number of the point midway between -2 and -8.
26. The distance between -10 and -3.

Simplify each of the following expressions.

27. $-\dfrac{-36}{4}$
28. $\dfrac{x}{-1}$
29. $-\dfrac{-x}{-y}$

Find the value of each of these expressions.

30. $-(-17 + 3)$
31. $6(-4) - 2(-3)$
32. $(-4)^2 + (-4)^3$
33. $(3 - 11)(11 - 3)$
34. $-5(6)(8) - 8(6)(5)$

The following problems are about the
functions $y = -2x$ and $y = x + 3$.

35. Make a table for each of these
functions. In each table, let $x = 0$,
1, 2, and 3.
36. Graph both functions on the same pair
of axes by plotting the points in the
tables and joining them with lines.
37. What are the coordinates of the point
in which the lines intersect?

Find the values of the following
expressions, given that $x = 9$ and $y = -2$.

38. $5(x + y)$

39. $xy + 1$

40. $x^2 - y^2$

If a ball is thrown upward at a speed of 160
feet per second, its velocity at any given
instant is given by the formula
$v = 160 - 32t$, in which t represents the
time in seconds and v represents its
upward velocity in feet per second.

Find the velocity of the ball after
41. 2 seconds.
42. 5 seconds.
43. 6 seconds.

44. What does your answer to problem 42
mean?
45. What does your answer to problem 43
mean?

Extra Credit.

A car was driven on a long trip. During
the trip, the five tires were rotated
regularly so that each one went the same
distance. How many miles did each tire
travel if the car went
1. 18,000 miles?
2. x miles?

ELEMENTARY ALGEBRA
Test on Chapter 3

Name _____

Read the following statements carefully and tell whether each is true or false.

1. The square of a negative number is positive.
2. If both coordinates of a point are negative, the point is in the third quadrant.
3. The opposite of every number is negative.
4. The product of a number and its opposite is zero.

Find each of the following.

5. The sum of -18 and 6.
6. The quotient of 24 and -4.
7. The difference between 12 and -3.
8. The product of -20 and -2.

Write each of the following statements in symbols, letting x represent the number.

9. A certain number is less than negative two.
10. Half a certain number is more than the square of the number.
11. The quotient of a certain number and three is equal to five.

Here are directions for a number trick and part of a table to show what happens if the trick is done with two different numbers.

Think of a number:	1	-7
Subtract three:	IIII	IIII
Multiply by four:	IIII	IIII
Add eight:	IIII	IIII
Divide by four:	IIII	IIII
Subtract the number that you first thought of:	IIII	IIII

12. Copy and complete the table.
13. Show how the trick works by illustrating the steps with boxes and circles. (Draw solid circles to represent negative numbers.)

What number should replace IIII in each of the following equations to make it true?

14. $-8 + IIII = 0$
15. $IIII - 4 = -1$
16. $-2(IIII) = -6$
17. $IIII + 3 = -4$
18. $\dfrac{IIII}{3} = -9$

Which of these symbols, >, =, or <, should replace IIII in each of the following?

19. $-9 + -9 + -9 \ IIII \ -9(-9)(-9)$
20. $18 - -12 \ IIII \ 18 + 12$
21. $-16 - 14 \ IIII \ -16(14)$
22. $(-37)^3 \ IIII \ (-37)^2$

Use a number line to find each of the following.

23. The number of the point midway between -2 and 8.
24. The distance between -8 and 5.
25. The number of the point midway between -1 and -7.
26. The distance between -6 and -1.

Simplify each of the following expressions.

27. $-\dfrac{42}{-7}$
28. $\dfrac{-x}{x}$
29. $-\dfrac{-y}{-1}$

Find the value of each of these expressions.

30. $-4(5)(9) - 9(5)(4)$
31. $2(-4) - 5(-3)$
32. $-(-32 + 5)$
33. $(-3)^2 + (-3)^3$
34. $(7 - 13)(13 - 7)$

The following problems are about the functions $y = x + 4$ and $y = -3x$.

35. Make a table for each of these functions. In each table, let $x = 0$, 1, 2, and 3.

36. Graph both functions on the same pair of axes by plotting the points in the tables and joining them with lines.

37. What are the coordinates of the point in which the lines intersect?

Find the values of the following expressions, given that $x = 7$ and $y = -4$.

38. $3(x + y)$

39. $x^2 - y^2$

40. $xy + 2$

If a ball is thrown upward at a speed of 128 feet per second, its velocity at any given instant is given by the formula $v = 128 - 32t$, in which t represents the time in seconds and v represents its upward velocity in feet per second.

Find the velocity of the ball after

41. 2 seconds.

42. 4 seconds.

43. 5 seconds.

44. What does your answer to problem 42 mean?

45. What does your answer to problem 43 mean?

Extra Credit.

A car was driven on a long trip. During the trip, the five tires were rotated regularly so that each one went the same distance. How many miles did each tire travel if the car went

1. 14,000 miles?

2. x miles?

ELEMENTARY ALGEBRA
Test on Chapter 3

Name_____

Read the following statements carefully and tell whether each is true or false.

1. Every integer is a counting number.
2. If the x-coordinate of a point is negative, the point is left of the y-axis.
3. The sum of two numbers is always more than either number.
4. The cube of a negative number is always negative.

Find each of the following.

5. The product of -18 and -6.
6. The sum of -24 and 4.
7. The quotient of 12 and -3.
8. The difference between 20 and -2.

Write each of the following statements in symbols, letting x represent the number.

9. A certain number is more than two.
10. The cube of a certain number is less than twice the number.
11. The difference between a certain number and four is equal to negative one.

Here are directions for a number trick and part of a table to show what happens if the trick is done with two different numbers.

Think of a number:	1	-7
Multiply by two:	||||	||||
Subtract ten:	||||	||||
Divide by two:	||||	||||
Add one:	||||	||||
Subtract the number that you first thought of:	||||	||||

12. Copy and complete the table.
13. Show how the trick works by illustrating the steps with boxes and circles. (Draw solid circles to represent negative numbers.)

What number should replace |||| in each of the following equations to make it true?

14. $|||| + 5 = -6$
15. $-3(||||) = -12$
16. $-9 + |||| = 0$
17. $\dfrac{||||}{2} = -8$
18. $|||| - 6 = -1$

Which of these symbols, >, =, or <, should replace |||| in each of the following?

19. $19 - -84 \; |||| \; 19 + 84$
20. $-15 - 11 \; |||| \; -15(11)$
21. $(-54)^2 \; |||| \; (-54)^3$
22. $-6(-6)(-6) \; |||| \; -6 + -6 + -6$

Use a number line to find each of the following.

23. The distance between -5 and 7.
24. The number of the point midway between -4 and 8.
25. The distance between -9 and -5.
26. The number of the point midway between -3 and -11.

Simplify each of the following expressions.

27. $- \dfrac{-56}{8}$
28. $\dfrac{0}{-x}$
29. $- \dfrac{-y}{-y}$

Find the value of each of these expressions.

30. $(5 - 12)(12 - 5)$
31. $-(-21 + 2)$
32. $-5(6)(7) - 7(6)(5)$
33. $2(-5) - 4(-3)$
34. $(-5)^2 + (-5)^3$

3Cl

The following problems are about the
functions $y = x + 6$ and $y = -2x$.

35. Make a table for each of these
    functions. In each table, let $x = 0$,
    1, 2, and 3.
36. Graph both functions on the same pair
    of axes by plotting the points in the
    tables and joining them with lines.
37. What are the coordinates of the point
    in which the lines intersect?

Find the values of the following
expressions, given that $x = 6$ and $y = -5$.

38. $4(x + y)$

39. $xy + 2$

40. $x^2 - y^2$

If a ball is thrown upward at a speed of 96
feet per second, its velocity at any given
instant is given by the formula
$v = 96 - 32t$, in which t represents the
time in seconds and v represents its
upward velocity in feet per second.

    Find the velocity of the ball after
41. 2 seconds.
42. 3 seconds.
43. 5 seconds.

44. What does your answer to problem 42
    mean?
45. What does your answer to problem 43
    mean?

Extra Credit.

A car was driven on a long trip. During
the trip, the five tires were rotated
regularly so that each one went the same
distance. How many miles did each tire
travel if the car went
 1. 12,000 miles?
 2. x miles?

ELEMENTARY ALGEBRA:
Test on Chapter 3

Name_____

Read the following statements carefully and tell whether each is true or false.

1. Every number is larger than its opposite.
2. If the x-coordinate of a point is negative, the point is below the x-axis.
3. Zero is an integer.
4. The sum of two negative numbers may be positive.

Find each of the following.

5. The quotient of 18 and -6.
6. The difference between 24 and -4.
7. The product of -12 and -3.
8. The sum of -20 and 2.

Write each of the following statements in symbols, letting x represent the number.

9. A certain number is less than two.
10. Twice a certain number is more than the cube of the number.
11. The quotient of a certain number and four is equal to negative one.

Here are directions for a number trick and part of a table to show what happens if the trick is done with two different numbers.

Think of a number:	1	-7
Multiply by three:	‖‖	‖‖
Subtract twelve:	‖‖	‖‖
Divide by three:	‖‖	‖‖
Add one:	‖‖	‖‖
Subtract the number that you first thought of:	‖‖	‖‖

12. Copy and complete the table.
13. Show how the trick works by illustrating the steps with boxes and circles. (Draw solid circles to represent negative numbers.)

What number should replace ‖‖ in each of the following equations to make it true?

14. $‖‖ - 8 = -1$
15. $\dfrac{‖‖}{3} = -12$
16. $‖‖ + 6 = -7$
17. $-2(‖‖) = -10$
18. $-4 + ‖‖ = 0$

Which of these symbols, >, =, or <, should replace ‖‖ in each of the following?

19. $17 - -76 \ ‖‖ \ 17 + 76$
20. $(-63)^2 \ ‖‖ \ (-63)^3$
21. $-7(-7)(-7) \ ‖‖ \ -7 + -7 + -7$
22. $-14 - 13 \ ‖‖ \ -14(13)$

Use a number line to find each of the following.

23. The distance between -9 and 1.
24. The number of the point midway between -3 and 5.
25. The distance between -6 and -2.
26. The number of the point midway between -4 and -10.

Simplify each of the following expressions.

27. $-\dfrac{48}{-6}$
28. $\dfrac{-x}{-1}$
29. $-\dfrac{-y}{-x}$

Find the value of each of these expressions.

30. $-3(5)(8) - 8(5)(3)$
31. $(-2)^3 + (-2)^4$
32. $5(-4) - 3(-2)$
33. $-(-29 + 4)$
34. $(5 - 14)(14 - 5)$

3D1

The following problems are about the functions $y = -x$ and $y = x - 4$.

35. Make a table for each of these functions. In each table, let $x = 0$, 1, 2, and 3.
36. Graph both functions on the same pair of axes by plotting the points in the tables and joining them with lines.
37. What are the coordinates of the point in which the lines intersect?

Find the values of the following expressions, given that $x = 8$ and $y = -3$.

38. $6(x + y)$
39. $x^2 - y^2$
40. $xy + 1$

If a ball is thrown upward at a speed of 192 feet per second, its velocity at any given instant is given by the formula $v = 192 - 32t$, in which t represents the time in seconds and v represents its upward velocity in feet per second.

Find the velocity of the ball after
41. 2 seconds.
42. 6 seconds.
43. 7 seconds.

44. What does your answer to problem 42 mean?
45. What does your answer to problem 43 mean?

Extra Credit.

A car was driven on a long trip. During the trip, the five tires were rotated regularly so that each one went the same distance. How many miles did each tire travel if the car went
1. 16,000 miles?
2. x miles?

ELEMENTARY ALGEBRA
Test on Chapter 4

Show that each of the following numbers is rational by writing it as the quotient of two integers.

1. -4   2. 0.7   3. $3\frac{1}{5}$

Change each of the following rational numbers to decimal form.

4. $\frac{9}{4}$ 5. $\frac{13}{-10}$ 6. $\frac{-2}{-16}$

Which of these symbols, >, =, or <, should replace ‖‖ in each of the following?

7. |0.3| ‖‖ |-0.3| 10. 7.2 ‖‖ 7.04

8. -5.1 ‖‖ -5   11. -6.5 ‖‖ -6.50

9. |-9| ‖‖ -9   12. -0.8 ‖‖ 0.08

Perform the operations indicated.

13. -3.7 + -7.3   19. -1.8 + 0.4

14. -3.7 - -7.3   20. 2(-0.25)

15. -6 + 0.2   21. $(-0.25)^2$

16. 0.6 + -2   22. $\frac{2}{-0.25}$

17. -1.8 - 0.4

18. -1.8(0.4)

What number should replace ‖‖ in each of the following equations to make it true?

23. 9(‖‖) = -0.9   26. -4.1(‖‖) = 0

24. ‖‖ + -0.5 = 8   27. $\frac{-3.6}{‖‖} = 1.2$

25. -4.1 + ‖‖ = 0

Here are directions for a number trick and part of a table to show what happens if the trick is done with three different numbers.

Think of a number:	2.1	-0.6	-7.3
Add five:	‖‖	‖‖	‖‖
Multiply by two:	‖‖	‖‖	‖‖
Subtract seven:	‖‖	‖‖	‖‖
Divide by two:	‖‖	‖‖	‖‖
Subtract the number that you first thought of:	‖‖	‖‖	‖‖

28. Copy and complete the table.
29. What number is the result of this trick?

Approximate each of the following numbers as indicated.

30. 7.08 to the nearest integer.
31. -5.16 to the nearest tenth.
32. 2.072 to the nearest hundredth.
33. -12.5 to the nearest integer.

Find an approximation in decimal form to the nearest hundredth for each of the following rational numbers.

34. $\frac{1}{27}$ 36. $\frac{19}{16}$

35. $\frac{10}{27}$ 37. $\frac{3}{1000}$

Make a table of numbers for each of the following functions and draw its graph. In each case, connect the points with either a line or a curve.

38. $y = x^2 - 5$
    Let x vary from -3 to 3.

39. $y = -3x + 7$
    Let x vary from 0 to 4.

40. $y = \frac{-4}{x}$
    Let x vary from -4 to 4.

41. $y = 2.5x$
    Let x vary from -3 to 3.

Compare the formulas of the functions in problems 38-41 with their graphs.

42. Which functions are linear?
43. Which one is a direct variation?
44. Which have graphs that are curves?
45. Which is an inverse variation?

Extra Credit.

Can you figure out what the 100th digit after the decimal point of $\frac{13}{14}$ is? If so, explain your reasoning.

ELEMENTARY ALGEBRA
Test on Chapter 4

Name _____

Show that each of the following numbers is rational by writing it as the quotient of two integers.

1. 0   2. -2.3   3. $6\frac{1}{4}$

Change each of the following rational numbers to decimal form.

4. $\frac{37}{-5}$ 5. $\frac{-2}{-8}$ 6. $\frac{12}{125}$

Which of these symbols, >, =, or <, should replace ⊪ in each of the following?

7. -0.9 ⊪ 0.1   10. -4.8 ⊪ -4.9

8. 7.2 ⊪ 7.20   11. 6.3 ⊪ 6.06

9. -5 ⊪ |-5| 12. |-1.7| ⊪ |1.7|

Perform the operations indicated.

13. -4.2 + 0.6   18. -2.8 - -8.2

14. -4.2 - 0.6   19. -7 + 0.4

15. -4.2(0.6)   20. 0.7 + -4

16. $\frac{-4.2}{-0.6}$ 21. 2(-0.31)

22. $(-0.31)^2$

17. -2.8 + -8.2

What number should replace ⊪ in each of the following equations to make it true?

23. 0.2(⊪) = -2

24. 1.8 + ⊪ = 0

25. 1.8(⊪) = 0

26. $\frac{-3.0}{⊪} = 1.5$

27. ⊪ + -0.4 = 7

Here are directions for a number trick and part of a table to show what happens if the trick is done with three different numbers.

Think of a number:	4.5	-0.2	-3.1
Subtract four:	⊪	⊪	⊪
Multiply by three:	⊪	⊪	⊪
Add six:	⊪	⊪	⊪
Divide by three:	⊪	⊪	⊪
Subtract the number that you first thought of:	⊪	⊪	⊪

28. Copy and complete the table.
29. What number is the result of this trick?

Approximate each of the following numbers as indicated.

30. 6.09 to the nearest integer.
31. -4.27 to the nearest tenth.
32. 1.854 to the nearest hundredth.
33. -0.5 to the nearest integer.

Find an approximation in decimal form to the nearest hundredth for each of the following rational numbers.

34. $\frac{1}{37}$ 36. $\frac{51}{16}$

35. $\frac{10}{37}$ 37. $\frac{1}{1000}$

Make a table of numbers for each of the following functions and draw its graph. In each case, connect the points with either a line or a curve.

38. y = -1.5x
    Let x vary from -3 to 3.

39. $y = x^2 + 2$
    Let x vary from -3 to 3.

40. y = 2x - 7
    Let x vary from 0 to 5.

41. $y = \frac{-5}{x}$
    Let x vary from -4 to 4.

Compare the formulas of the functions in problems 38-41 with their graphs.

42. Which functions are linear?
43. Which one is a direct variation?
44. Which have graphs that are curves?
45. Which is an inverse variation?

Extra Credit.

Can you figure out what the 100th digit after the decimal point of $\frac{9}{14}$ is? If so, explain your reasoning.

ELEMENTARY ALGEBRA
Test on Chapter 4

Name _____

Show that each of the following numbers is rational by writing it as the quotient of two integers.

1. -1   2. 0.67   3. $4\frac{1}{2}$

Change each of the following rational numbers to decimal form.

4. $\frac{-21}{6}$ 5. $\frac{9}{100}$ 6. $\frac{-5}{-8}$

Which of these symbols, >, =, or <, should replace IIII in each of the following?

7. 10.2 IIII 10.12   10. -9.1 IIII 0.91

8. |-3.5| IIII |3.5| 11. -2.6 IIII -2.7

9. 0.4 IIII 0.10   12. -8.30 IIII -8.3

Perform the operations indicated.

13. 2(-0.14)   19. -2.4 + 0.8

14. $(-0.14)^2$ 20. -2.4 - 0.8

15. -4.6 + -7.6   21. -2.4(0.8)

16. -4.6 - -7.6   22. $\frac{-2.4}{0.8}$

17. -5 + 0.3

18. 0.5 + -3

What number should replace IIII in each of the following equations to make it true?

23. IIII + -0.2 = 6   26. -3.2 + IIII = 0

24. 0.5(IIII) = -5   27. -3.2(IIII) = 0

25. $\frac{8.4}{IIII}$ = -2.1

Here are directions for a number trick and part of a table to show what happens if the trick is done with three different numbers.

Think of a number:	3.7	0.4	-1.6
Multiply by two:	IIII	IIII	IIII
Subtract seven:	IIII	IIII	IIII
Divide by two:	IIII	IIII	IIII
Add four:	IIII	IIII	IIII
Subtract the number that you first thought of:	IIII	IIII	IIII

28. Copy and complete the table.
29. What number is the result of this trick?

Approximate each of the following numbers as indicated.

30. 9.07 to the nearest integer.
31. -2.48 to the nearest tenth.
32. 3.163 to the nearest hundredth.
33. -8.5 to the nearest integer.

Find an approximation in decimal form to the nearest hundredth for each of the following rational numbers.

34. $\frac{1}{19}$ 36. $\frac{3}{1000}$

35. $\frac{10}{19}$ 37. $\frac{35}{32}$

Make a table of numbers for each of the following functions and draw its graph. In each case, connect the points with either a line or a curve.

38. $y = \frac{6}{x}$
Let x vary from -4 to 4.

39. $y = 1.5x$
Let x vary from -3 to 3.

40. $y = 4 - x^2$
Let x vary from -3 to 3.

41. $y = -2x + 5$
Let x vary from 0 to 5.

Compare the formulas of the functions in problems 38-41 with their graphs.

42. Which functions are linear?
43. Which one is a direct variation?
44. Which have graphs that are curves?
45. Which is an inverse variation?

Extra Credit.

Can you figure out what the 100th digit after the decimal point of $\frac{5}{14}$ is? If so, explain your reasoning.

4C

ELEMENTARY ALGEBRA
Test on Chapter 4

Name _____

Show that each of the following numbers is rational by writing it as the quotient of two integers.

1. 5
2. -0.08
3. $2\frac{1}{3}$

Change each of the following rational numbers to decimal form.

4. $\frac{-7}{-10}$
5. $\frac{25}{4}$
6. $\frac{9}{-24}$

Which of these symbols, >, =, or <, should replace ‖‖ in each of the following?

7. 0.05 ‖‖ 0.4
8. 1.2 ‖‖ -8
9. -3.6 ‖‖ -3.60
10. |5.7| ‖‖ |-5.7|
11. -2 ‖‖ |-2|
12. -9.4 ‖‖ -9.5

Perform the operations indicated.

13. -4 + 0.9
14. 0.4 + -9
15. -3.6 + 0.3
16. -3.6 - 0.3
17. -3.6(0.3)
18. $\frac{-3.6}{-0.3}$
19. -1.7 + -5.7
20. -1.7 - -5.7
21. $(-0.18)^2$
22. 2(-0.18)

What number should replace ‖‖ in each of the following equations to make it true?

23. 2.6 + ‖‖ = 0
24. 2.6(‖‖) = 0
25. ‖‖ - 0.1 = 5
26. $\frac{3.4}{‖‖}$ = -1.7
27. 0.8(‖‖) = -8

Here are directions for a number trick and part of a table to show what happens if the trick is done with three different numbers.

Think of a number:	7.2	0.6	-1.8
Divide by two:	‖‖	‖‖	‖‖
Subtract three:	‖‖	‖‖	‖‖
Multiply by two:	‖‖	‖‖	‖‖
Add five:	‖‖	‖‖	‖‖
Subtract the number that you first thought of:	‖‖	‖‖	‖‖

28. Copy and complete the table.
29. What number is the result of this trick?

Approximate each of the following numbers as indicated.

30. 8.06 to the nearest integer.
31. -3.19 to the nearest tenth.
32. 4.572 to the nearest hundredth.
33. -6.5 to the nearest integer.

Find an approximation in decimal form to the nearest hundredth for each of the following rational numbers.

34. $\frac{1}{77}$
35. $\frac{10}{77}$
36. $\frac{1}{1000}$
37. $\frac{23}{16}$

Make a table of numbers for each of the following functions and draw its graph. In each case, connect the points with either a line or curve.

38. y = 3x - 4
   Let x vary from 0 to 4.

39. y = -2.5x
   Let x vary from -3 to 3.

40. $y = \frac{5}{x}$
   Let x vary from -4 to 4.

41. $y = 7 - x^2$
   Let x vary from -3 to 3.

Compare the formulas of the functions in problems 38-41 with their graphs.

42. Which functions are linear?
43. Which one is a direct variation?
44. Which have graphs that are curves?
45. Which is an inverse variation?

Extra Credit.

Can you figure out what the 100th digit after the decimal point of $\frac{1}{14}$ is? If so, explain your reasoning.

4D

ELEMENTARY ALGEBRA
Test on Chapter 5

Name_____

Tell whether each of the following equations is true, false, or neither.

1. $3^2 - 2^3 = 1$ 2. $2x - 1 = x$

If possible, find a number that can replace x in each of the following equations to make it true. If you think that no such number can be found, briefly explain why.

3. $-6x = 12$ 5. $x = 2x$

4. $3 - x = -7$

Tell which of the following numbers are solutions of the equation given.

6. $x^2 = 6 - x$ 2, 3, 6, -2, -3, -6

7. $x(x + 4) = 0$ 0, 1, 4, -1, -4

What operations should be performed on each of these expressions to give x as the result?

8. $5x - 2$ 9. $\dfrac{x + 9}{4}$

Solve each of the following equations for x.

10. $x + 10 = -2.5$

11. $-2.5x = 10$

12. $\dfrac{x}{10} = -2.5$

Use the property named to write another expression equivalent to $x(x - 5)$.

13. Distributive property of multiplication over subtraction.

14. Commutative property of multiplication.

Write a simpler expression equivalent to each of the following.

15. $7 + (x + 2)$ 18. $4x + 4x$

16. $5x - x$ 19. $4 \cdot x \cdot x$

17. $6(3x)$

Solve the following equations for x.

20. $2x + 9 = -5$ 22. $14 - 3x = 38$

21. $\dfrac{x}{3} - 8 = 12$ 23. $8x = 2x + 3$

24. $5(x - 3) = 3(x - 5)$

Find the lengths of the sides of the following figures.

25.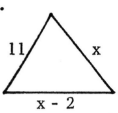
Perimeter is 39

26.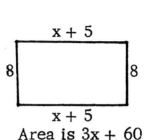
Area is 3x + 60

Find the length of each segment in this diagram. AB and CD are the same length.

A•————————E•————•B
    4(x - 1)   x
C•——————————————•D
       9x - 32

27. Length of AE.   29. Length of CD.
28. Length of EB.

In a horse race, Citation is 51 feet ahead of Whirlaway. While Citation is running at a speed of 48 feet per second, Whirlaway speeds up to 54 feet per second. Find out how long it will take Whirlaway to catch up by doing each of the following.

30. If x represents the time it takes Whirlaway to catch up, what distance does each horse run during this time? (Give your answers in terms of x.)

31. Draw a diagram to represent the problem.

32. Use the information in your diagram to write an equation.

33. Solve the equation for x.

34. How far did each horse run during this time?

Extra Credit.

In six years, Clem Kadiddlehopper will be five times as old as he was 26 years ago. How old is he now?

5A

ELEMENTARY ALGEBRA
Test on Chapter 5

Tell whether each of the following equations is true, false, or neither.

1. $(5 + 2)^2 = 5^2 + 2^2$

2. $3(x - 4) = 3x - 12$

If possible, find a number that can replace x in each of the following equations to make it true. If you think that no such number can be found, briefly explain why.

3. $5 - x = -10$ 5. $x = x + 4$

4. $-2x = 6$

Tell which of the following numbers are solutions of the equation given.

6. $x^2 - 8 = 2x$ $2, 4, 8, -2, -4, -8$

7. $x(x + 5) = 0$ $0, 1, 5, -1, -5$

What operations should be performed on each of these expressions to give x as the result?

8. $2x - 5$ 9. $\dfrac{x + 4}{9}$

Solve each of the following equations for x.

10. $x + 12 = -1.5$ 12. $\dfrac{x}{12} = -1.5$

11. $-1.5x = 12$

Use the property named to write another expression equivalent to $x(x - 6)$.

13. Commutative property of multiplication.

14. Distributive property of multiplication over subtraction.

Write a simpler expression equivalent to each of the following.

15. $4x - x$ 18. $6 \cdot x \cdot x$

16. $10(2x)$ 19. $6x + 6x$

17. $5 + (x + 3)$

Solve the following equations for x.

20. $3x + 11 = -4$ 21. $25 - 2x = 47$

22. $\dfrac{x}{4} - 9 = 7$ 24. $9x = 1 + 5x$

23. $8(x - 5) = 5(x - 8)$

Find the lengths of the sides of the following figures.

25.

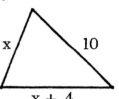

Perimeter is 38

26.

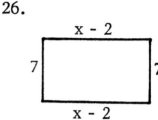

Area is $3x + 30$

Find the length of each segment in this diagram. AB and CD are the same length.

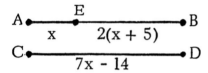

27. Length of AE.   29. Length of CD.
28. Length of EB.

In a horse race, Citation is 52 feet ahead of Whirlaway. While Citation is running at a speed of 47 feet per second, Whirlaway speeds up to 55 feet per second. Find out how long it will take Whirlaway to catch up by doing each of the following.

30. If x represents the time it takes Whirlaway to catch up, what distance does each horse run during this time? (Give your answers in terms of x.)
31. Draw a diagram to represent the problem.
32. Use the information in your diagram to write an equation.
33. Solve the equation for x.
34. How far did each horse run during this time?

Extra Credit.

In seven years, Clem Kadiddlehopper will be six times as old as he was 23 years ago. How old is he now?

5B

ELEMENTARY ALGEBRA
Test on Chapter 5

Name_____

Tell whether each of the following equations is true, false, or neither.

1. $3x - 2 = x$

2. $(7 + 3)^2 = 7^2 + 3^2$

If possible, find a number that can replace x in each of the following equations to make it true. If you think that no such number can be found, briefly explain why.

3. $x + 3 = -4$ 5. $-4x = 8$

4. $x = x - 10$

Tell which of the following numbers are solutions of the equation given.

6. $x = x^2 - 6$ 2, 3, 6, -2, -3, -6

7. $x(x + 8) = 0$ 0, 1, 8, -1, -8

What operations should be performed on each of these expressions to give x as the result?

8. $3x + 2$

9. $\dfrac{x - 7}{5}$

Solve each of the following equations for x.

10. $x + 7 = -3.5$

11. $-3.5x = 7$

12. $\dfrac{x}{7} = -3.5$

Use the property named to write another expression equivalent to $x(x + 8)$.

13. Distributive property of multiplication over addition.

14. Commutative property of multiplication.

Write a simpler expression equivalent to each of the following.

15. $5x + 5x$

16. $5 \cdot x \cdot x$

17. $8 + (x + 3)$

18. $6x - x$

19. $4(2x)$

Solve the following equations for x.

20. $4x + 7 = -9$

21. $\dfrac{x}{2} - 17 = 7$

22. $15 - 6x = 87$ 24. $5x = 3x - 1$

23. $9(x + 4) = 4(x + 9)$

Find the lengths of the sides of the following figures.

25.
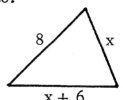

Perimeter is 36

26.
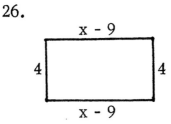

Area is $2x - 6$

Find the length of each segment in this diagram. AB and CD are the same length.

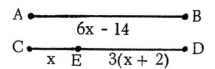

27. Length of AB.   29. Length of ED.
28. Length of CE.

In a horse race, Citation is 57 feet ahead of Whirlaway. While Citation is running at a speed of 45 feet per second, Whirlaway speeds up to 51 feet per second. Find out how long it will take Whirlaway to catch up by doing each of the following.

30. If x represents the time it takes Whirlaway to catch up, what distance does each horse run during this time? (Give your answers in terms of x.)

31. Draw a diagram to represent the problem.

32. Use the information in your diagram to write an equation.

33. Solve the equation for x.

34. How far did each horse run during this time?

Extra Credit.

In nine years, Clem Kadiddlehopper will be eight times as old as he was 26 years ago. How old is he now?

ELEMENTARY ALGEBRA
Test on Chapter 5

Name_____

Tell whether each of the following equations is true, false, or neither.

1. $x^2 + x = 2$

2. $\dfrac{12 - 4}{4} = \dfrac{12}{4} - \dfrac{4}{4}$

If possible, find a number that can replace x in each of the following equations to make it true. If you think that no such number can be found, briefly explain why.

3. $x + 5 = -1$

4. $\dfrac{x}{8} = 16$

5. $-3x = 12$

Tell which of the following numbers are solutions of the equation given.

6. $x^2 = 3x + 4$ 1, 3, 4, -1, -3, -4

7. $x(6 - x) = 0$ 0, 1, 6, -1, -6

What operations should be performed on each of these expressions to give x as the result?

8. $2x + 3$

9. $\dfrac{x - 5}{7}$

Solve each of the following equations for x.

10. $x + 9 = -1.8$

11. $-1.8x = 9$

12. $\dfrac{x}{9} = -1.8$

Use the property named to write another expression equivalent to $x(x + 3)$.

13. Commutative property of multiplication.

14. Distributive property of multiplication over addition.

Write a simpler expression equivalent to each of the following.

15. $7(2x)$

16. $3 \cdot x \cdot x$

17. $3x + 3x$

18. $4 + (x + 9)$

19. $8x - x$

Solve the following equations for x.

20. $2x + 13 = -3$

21. $18 - 4x = 42$

22. $6(x + 2) = 2(x + 6)$

23. $\dfrac{x}{5} - 7 = 14$

24. $8x = 3x + 1$

Find the lengths of the sides of the following figures.

25.

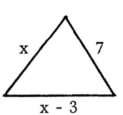

Perimeter is 34

26.

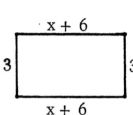

Area is 8x - 7

Find the length of each segment in this diagram. AB and CD are the same length.

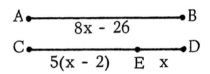

27. Length of AB.
28. Length of CE.
29. Length of ED.

In a horse race, Citation is 44 feet ahead of Whirlaway. While Citation is running at a speed of 42 feet per second, Whirlaway speeds up to 50 feet per second. Find out how long it will take Whirlaway to catch up by doing each of the following.

30. If x represents the time it takes Whirlaway to catch up, what distance does each horse run during this time? (Give your answers in terms of x.)
31. Draw a diagram to represent the problem.
32. Use the information in your diagram to write an equation.
33. Solve the equation for x.
34. How far did each horse run during this time?

Extra Credit.

In five years, Clem Kadiddlehopper will be four times as old as he was 19 years ago. How old is he now?

ELEMENTARY ALGEBRA
Test on Chapter 6

Name _____

Find the values of the following expressions when x and y are replaced by the ordered pairs given.

1. $3x + 5y$ (-9, 5)

2. $x - y^2$ (3, -7)

Tell whether or not each of the following ordered pairs is a solution of the equation $x^2 - 3y = 13$.

3. (2, -3)

4. (-4, 1)

Find every pair of positive integers that can replace x and y in each of the following equations to make it true.

5. $x + 5y = 14$

6. $xy = 121$

Solve each of the following equations for the variable indicated.

7. $3x = y + 5$ for x

8. $x + 4y = 6$ for y

A formula used in physics in studying electricity is $i = \dfrac{e}{r}$.

9. Solve this formula for e.
10. Solve the formula that you have just written for r.

A new candle 24 centimeters tall burns at the rate of 5 centimeters per hour.

11. Write a formula for its height, h, after it has been burning t hours.
12. Find the height of the candle after it has burned 3 hours.

Write each of the following equations in standard form and give the values of a, b, and c.

13. $x = 3y + 9$

14. $2(x - 5) = 10$

Find the x- and y-intercepts of the lines having the following equations.

15. $9x - 2y = 36$

16. $\dfrac{x}{5} + \dfrac{y}{8} = 2$

Plot the following points, draw a line through each pair, and find its slope.

17. (0, -3) and (5, -1)

18. (1, 6) and (3, -2)

Draw graphs of the following lines.

19. The line through the origin having a slope of $\dfrac{1}{4}$.

20. The line through (-5, 2) having a slope of -3.

What are the slopes and y-intercepts of the lines having the following equations?

21. $y = 7x - 3$

22. $y = \dfrac{1}{2}$

Graph the following equations.

23. $3x - 4y = -12$

24. $2x + y = 0$

25. $y = \dfrac{3}{2}x + 1$

Extra Credit.

Find a pair of positive integers that can replace x and y in the equation $31x + 37y = 700$ to make it true.

6A

ELEMENTARY ALGEBRA
Test on Chapter 6

Name _____

Find the values of the following expressions when x and y are replaced by the ordered pairs given.

1. $3x + 5y$ $(-7, 4)$

2. $x - y^2$ $(3, -8)$

Tell whether or not each of the following ordered pairs is a solution of the equation $x^2 - 3y = 7$.

3. $(4, -3)$

4. $(-5, 6)$

Find every pair of positive integers that can replace x and y in each of the following equations to make it true.

5. $xy = 49$

6. $x + 6y = 15$

Solve each of the following equations for the variable indicated.

7. $2x = y - 5$ for x

8. $x + 6y = 4$ for y

A formula used in chemistry in studying gases is $p = \dfrac{k}{v}$.

9. Solve this formula for k.
10. Solve the formula that you have just written for v.

A new candle 21 centimeters tall burns at the rate of 4 centimeters per hour.

11. Write a formula for its height, h, after it has been burning t hours.
12. Find the height of the candle after it has burned 2 hours.

Write each of the following equations in standard form and give the values of a, b, and c.

13. $x = 8 - 2y$

14. $3(y + 1) = 16$

Find the x- and y-intercepts of the lines having the following equations.

15. $5x + 4y = 40$

16. $\dfrac{x}{3} - \dfrac{y}{7} = 5$

Plot the following points, draw a line through each pair, and find its slope.

17. $(-2, -3)$ and $(3, 0)$

18. $(1, 2)$ and $(4, -4)$

Draw graphs of the following lines.

19. The line through the origin having a slope of $\dfrac{2}{3}$.

20. The line through $(-4, 3)$ having a slope of -2.

What are the slopes and y-intercepts of the lines having the following equations?

21. $y = 3x - 7$

22. $y = -x$

Graph the following equations.

23. $4x + 3y = -12$

24. $2x - y = 0$

25. $y = \dfrac{1}{5}x + 1$

Extra Credit.

Find a pair of positive integers that can replace x and y in the equation $41x + 89y = 800$ to make it true.

6B

ELEMENTARY ALGEBRA
Test on Chapter 6

Name _____

Find the values of the following expressions when x and y are replaced by the ordered pairs given.

1. $3x + 5y$ $\quad$ (-6, 2)

2. $x - y^2$ $\quad$ (3, -9)

Tell whether or not each of the following ordered pairs is a solution of the equation $x^2 - 3y = 10$.

3. (-1, -3)

4. (4, -2) ·

Find every pair of positive integers that can replace x and y in each of the following equations to make it true.

5. $x + 9y = 21$

6. $xy = 25$

Solve each of the following equations for the variable indicated.

7. $5x = y + 3$ for x

8. $x + 2y = 8$ for y

A formula used in physics in studying forces is $f = \dfrac{w}{s}$.

9. Solve this formula for w.

10. Solve the formula that you have just written for s.

A new candle 20 centimeters tall burns at the rate of 3 centimeters per hour.

11. Write a formula for its height, h, after it has been burning t hours.

12. Find the height of the candle after it has burned 4 hours.

Write each of the following equations in standard form and give the values of a, b, and c.

13. $y = 6 - 4x$

14. $5(x + 2) = 12$

Find the x- and y-intercepts of the lines having the following equations.

15. $2x + 7y = 28$

16. $\dfrac{x}{6} - \dfrac{y}{4} = 3$

Plot the following points, draw a line through each pair, and find its slope.

17. (0, -2) and (5, 2)

18. (1, 5) and (3, -1)

Draw graphs of the following lines.

19. The line through the origin having a slope of $\dfrac{3}{2}$.

20. The line through (-2, 5) having a slope of -1.

What are the slopes and y-intercepts of the lines having the following equations?

21. $y = 2x - 9$

22. $y = \dfrac{1}{5}$

Graph the following equations.

23. $2x - 6y = -12$

24. $3x - y = 0$

25. $y = \dfrac{1}{4}x + 3$

Extra Credit.

Find a pair of positive integers that can replace x and y in the equation $43x + 109y = 800$ to make it true.

ELEMENTARY ALGEBRA
Test on Chapter 6

Name _____

Find the values of the following expressions when x and y are replaced by the ordered pairs given.

1. $3x + 5y$ $(-8, 3)$

2. $x - y^2$ $(5, -6)$

Tell whether or not each of the following ordered pairs is a solution of the equation $x^2 - 3y = 15$.

3. $(6, -7)$

4. $(-3, -2)$

Find every pair of positive integers that can replace x and y in each of the following equations to make it true.

5. $xy = 9$

6. $x + 8y = 20$

Solve each of the following equations for the variable indicated.

7. $4x = y - 1$ for x

8. $x + 5y = 7$ for y

A formula used in economics in calculating interest rates is $r = \dfrac{i}{p}$.

9. Solve this formula for i.

10. Solve the formula that you have just written for p.

A new candle 17 centimeters tall burns at the rate of 2 centimeters per hour.

11. Write a formula for its height, h, after it has been burning t hours.

12. Find the height of the candle after it has burned 6 hours.

Write each of the following equations in standard form and give the values of a, b, and c.

13. $2x = 10 - y$

14. $4(y + 3) = 17$

Find the x- and y-intercepts of the lines having the following equations.

15. $3x - 5y = 30$

16. $\dfrac{x}{9} + \dfrac{y}{2} = 4$

Plot the following points, draw a line through each pair, and find its slope.

17. $(-3, -1)$ and $(3, 0)$

18. $(0, 6)$ and $(2, -4)$

Draw graphs of the following lines.

19. The line through the origin having a slope of $\dfrac{1}{2}$.

20. The line through $(-3, 4)$ having a slope of -4.

What are the slopes and y-intercepts of the lines having the following equations?

21. $y = 9x - 2$

22. $y = x$

Graph the following equations.

23. $6x + 2y = -12$

24. $x + 4y = 0$

25. $y = \dfrac{1}{3}x + 2$

Extra Credit.

Find a pair of positive integers that can replace x and y in the equation $37x + 57y = 800$ to make it true.

ELEMENTARY ALGEBRA
Test on Chapter 7

Name _____

Tell whether or not each of the following ordered pairs is a solution of these simultaneous equations.

$$2x + y = 2$$
$$y = 5 - x^2$$

1. (-1, 4)
2. (4, -6)

Write the equation that results from performing the following operations on these equations.

$$5x + 6y = 21$$
$$4x - 6y = 12$$

3. Adding the two equations.
4. Subtracting the second equation from the first.
5. Dividing both sides of the second equation by two.

Solve the following simultaneous equations by addition or subtraction.

6. $2x - y = 5$
   $2x + y = 33$

7. $x + 5y = 29$
   $-3x + 5y = 53$

8. $7x + 4y = 44$
   $6x + 5y = 33$

Graph the following pairs of simultaneous equations and tell what you can about the solutions of each.

9. $x + y = 2$
   $x - 3y = 6$

10. $y = x + 4$
    $y = -2x + 4$

11. $2y - x = 6$
    $y = \frac{1}{2}x - 1$

Solve the following simultaneous equations by substitution.

12. $8x - y = 21$
    $y = 5x$

13. $y - 3 = x$
    $4x + 7y = 10$

14. $2y - 3x = 29$
    $6x = y - 1$

The diagram below represents weights balanced on a seesaw. The distance between the weights is 14.

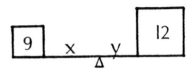

15. Write a pair of simultaneous equations for the diagram.
16. Solve the equations to find x and y.

Twelve reindeer pull a sled carrying a very stout man and a load of packages that weighs 1,840 pounds. Some of the packages weigh 7 pounds each, the rest weigh 12 pounds each, and there are 220 packages in all.

17. Letting x and y represent the numbers of packages weighing 7 and 12 pounds respectively, write a pair of equations, one relating the numbers of packages and the other relating their weights.
18. Solve the equations.
19. How many packages of each weight are on the sled?

Extra Credit.

Solve this set of simultaneous equations.

$$2x + y + z = 28$$
$$x + 2y + z = 17$$
$$x + y + 2z = 35$$

ELEMENTARY ALGEBRA
Test on Chapter 7

Name_____

Tell whether or not each of the following ordered pairs is a solution of these simultaneous equations.

$$2x + y = 1$$
$$y = x^2 - 2$$

1. (2, -3)
2. (-3, 7)

Write the equation that results from performing the following operations on these equations.

$$10x + 2y = 22$$
$$8x - 2y = 14$$

3. Adding the two equations.
4. Subtracting the second equation from the first.
5. Dividing both sides of the second equation by two.

Solve the following simultaneous equations by addition or subtraction.

6. $4x - y = 5$
    $4x + y = 31$

7. $x + 3y = 7$
    $-4x + 3y = 47$

8. $7x + 4y = 55$
    $5x + 6y = 33$

Graph the following pairs of simultaneous equations and tell what you can about the solutions of each.

9. $5x - 2y = -10$
    $x + y = 5$

10. $x + 2y = -2$
    $y = -\frac{1}{2}x - 1$

11. $y = -2x + 1$
    $y = x + 4$

Solve the following simultaneous equations by substitution.

12. $5y - x = 27$
    $x = 2y$

13. $x - 6 = y$
    $3x + 8y = 7$

14. $2x - 3y = 24$
    $7y = x - 1$

The diagram below represents weights balanced on a seesaw. The distance between the weights is 15.

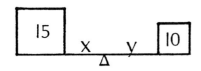

15. Write a pair of simultaneous equations for the diagram.
16. Solve the equations to find x and y.

Twelve reindeer pull a sled carrying a very stout man and a load of packages that weighs 1,570 pounds. Some of the packages weigh 6 pounds each, the rest weigh 13 pounds each, and there are 180 packages in all.

17. Letting x and y represent the numbers of packages weighing 6 and 13 pounds respectively, write a pair of equations, one relating the numbers of packages and the other relating their weights.
18. Solve the equations.
19. How many packages of each weight are on the sled?

Extra Credit.

Solve this set of simultaneous equations.

$$2x + y + z = 29$$
$$x + 2y + z = 18$$
$$x + y + 2z = 33$$

ELEMENTARY ALGEBRA
Test on Chapter 7

Name_____

Tell whether or not each of the following ordered pairs is a solution of these simultaneous equations.

$$y - x = 4$$
$$x = y^2 - 6$$

1. $(-2, 2)$
2. $(-5, -1)$

Write the equation that results from performing the following operations on these equations.

$$.7x + 10y = 24$$
$$6x - 10y = 8$$

3. Adding the two equations.
4. Subtracting the second equation from the first.
5. Dividing **both** sides of the second equation by two.

Solve the following simultaneous equations by addition or subtraction.

6. $x - 2y = 1$
   $x + 2y = 31$

7. $4x + 2y = 26$
   $4x - 3y = 51$

8. $4x + 5y = 32$
   $7x + 6y = 34$

Graph the following pairs of simultaneous equations and tell what you can about the solutions of each.

9. $y = -2x - 5$
   $y = x - 2$

10. $2x - y = 2$
    $y = 2x + 3$

11. $x + y = 4$
    $3x - 4y = 12$

Solve the following simultaneous equations by substitution.

12. $9x - y = 40$
    $y = 4x$

13. $y - 5 = x$
    $6x + 7y = 9$

14. $2y - 3x = 28$
    $8x = y - 1$

The diagram below represents weights balanced on a seesaw. The sum of the weights is 32.

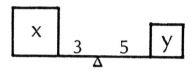

15. Write a pair of simultaneous equations for the diagram.
16. Solve the equations to find x and y.

Twelve reindeer pull a sled carrying a very stout man and a load of packages that weighs 1,870 pounds. Some of the packages weigh 8 pounds each, the rest weigh 15 pounds each, and there are 190 packages in all.

17. Letting x and y represent the numbers of packages weighing 8 and 15 pounds respectively, write a pair of equations, one relating the numbers of packages and the other relating their weights.
18. Solve the equations.
19. How many packages of each weight are on the sled?

Extra Credit.

Solve this set of simultaneous equations.

$$2x + y + z = 22$$
$$x + 2y + z = 11$$
$$x + y + 2z = 27$$

ELEMENTARY ALGEBRA
Test on Chapter 7

Name _____

Tell whether or not each of the following ordered pairs is a solution of these simultaneous equations.

$$y = x + 1$$
$$x + y^2 = 4$$

1. (1, 2)
2. (-4, -3)

Write the equation that results from performing the following operations on these equations.

$$7x + 8y = 32$$
$$2x - 8y = 18$$

3. Adding the two equations.
4. Subtracting the second equation from the first.
5. Dividing both sides of the second equation by two.

Solve the following simultaneous equations by addition or subtraction.

6. $x - 4y = 4$
$x + 4y = 32$

7. $5x + 6y = 17$
$5x - y = 38$

8. $6x + 7y = 39$
$5x + 4y = 16$

Graph the following pairs of simultaneous equations and tell what you can about the solutions of each.

9. $y = x + 5$
$y = -2x - 4$

10. $x + y = 3$
$3x - 5y = -15$

11. $x - 2y = 6$
$y = \frac{1}{2}x - 3$

Solve the following simultaneous equations by substitution.

12. $7y - x = 32$
$x = 3y$

13. $x - 4 = y$
$7x + 5y = 16$

14. $2x - 3y = 29$
$6y = x - 1$

The diagram below represents weights balanced on a seesaw. The sum of the weights is 30.

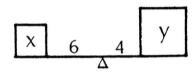

15. Write a pair of simultaneous equations for the diagram.
16. Solve the equations to find x and y.

Twelve reindeer pull a sled carrying a very stout man and a load of packages that weighs 1,770 pounds. Some of the packages weigh 5 pounds each, the rest weigh 14 pounds each, and there are 210 packages in all.

17. Letting x and y represent the numbers of packages weighing 5 and 14 pounds respectively, write a pair of equations, one relating the numbers of packages and the other relating their weights.
18. Solve the equations.
19. How many packages of each weight are on the sled?

Extra Credit.

Solve this set of simultaneous equations.

$$2x + y + z = 21$$
$$x + 2y + z = 10$$
$$x + y + 2z = 29$$

ELEMENTARY ALGEBRA
Test on Chapter 8

Name_____

Write each of the following numbers in the form indicated.

1. Ten billion as a power of ten.
2. The number that is ten times as large as 9×10^7 in scientific notation.
3. The number that is one-tenth as large as 10^{-5} as a power of ten.

Write each of the following numbers in decimal form.

4. 2.5×10^4
5. 8.01×10^{-5}

Write each of the following numbers in scientific notation.

6. $4,000$
7. 39×10^6
8. 0.00017
9. 0.5×10^{-12}

Write each of the following numbers without using any exponents.

10. $(-3)^5$
11. $(-7)^0$
12. 2^{-4}
13. $(-6)^{-1}$

Write each of the following expressions as a single power of x.

14. $x^{-8} \cdot x^3$
15. $(x^{-8})^3$
16. $\dfrac{x^2}{x^{-5}}$
17. $\dfrac{x^{-9}}{x^{-4}}$

Which of these symbols, $>$, $=$, or $<$, should replace ⅠⅠⅠⅠ in each of the following?

18. 10^{-8} ⅠⅠⅠⅠ 10^{-7}
19. 15^{-1} ⅠⅠⅠⅠ 3^1
20. $(-4)^0$ ⅠⅠⅠⅠ 4^0
21. $(-9)^2$ ⅠⅠⅠⅠ 2^{-9}

Write an expression without parentheses equivalent to each of the following.

22. $(2x)^6$
23. $(-y^7)^3$
24. $\left(\dfrac{x^2}{y}\right)^4$

Find each of the following products, quotients, or powers. Express each answer in scientific notation.

25. $(6 \times 10^6)(7 \times 10^7)$
26. $(5)(3 \times 10^5)$
27. $\dfrac{4 \times 10^4}{8 \times 10^1}$
28. $(7 \times 10^4)^3$

Which of these symbols, $>$, $=$, or $<$, should replace ⅠⅠⅠⅠ in each of the following?

29. $3^2 + 5^2$ ⅠⅠⅠⅠ 8^2
30. $3^2 \cdot 5^2$ ⅠⅠⅠⅠ 8^2
31. $2^3 \cdot 2^5$ ⅠⅠⅠⅠ 2^8
32. $(2^3)^5$ ⅠⅠⅠⅠ 2^8

Find x in each of the following equations.

33. $6^2 \cdot 6^7 = 6^x$
34. $2^6 \cdot 7^6 = x^6$
35. $\dfrac{15^4}{5^4} = x^4$
36. $\dfrac{4^{15}}{4^5} = 4^x$

The average distances of Pluto and Jupiter from the sun are 3.7 billion and 490 million miles respectively.

37. Write each of these distances in scientific notation.
38. How many times farther from the sun is Pluto than Jupiter?

The following problems are about the exponential function $y = 1.5(2^x)$.

39. Make a table for this function, letting $x = 0, 1, 2,$ and 3.
40. Graph the function by plotting the points and connecting them with a smooth curve.

Extra Credit.

How long do you think it would take you to walk one million inches?

8A

ELEMENTARY ALGEBRA
Test on Chapter 8

Name _____

Write each of the following numbers in the form indicated.

1. One hundred million as a power of ten.
2. The number that is ten times as large as 9×10^6 in scientific notation.
3. The number that is one-tenth as large as 10^{-4} as a power of ten.

Write each of the following numbers in decimal form.

4. 2.5×10^5 5. 8.01×10^{-3}

Write each of the following numbers in scientific notation.

6. 400 8. 0.000017
7. 39×10^4 9. 0.5×10^{-11}

Write each of the following numbers without using any exponents.

10. $(-4)^0$ 12. $(-2)^7$
11. 5^{-3} 13. $(-8)^{-1}$

Write each of the following expressions as a single power of x.

14. $x^{-6} \cdot x^5$ 17. $\dfrac{x^{-10}}{x^{-7}}$
15. $(x^{-6})^5$
16. $\dfrac{x^3}{x^{-8}}$

Which of these symbols, $>$, $=$, or $<$, should replace ||| in each of the following?

18. 10^{-8} ||| 10^{-9} 20. 4^{-5} ||| $(-5)^4$
19. 2^1 ||| 13^{-1} 21. $(-7)^0$ ||| 7^0

Write an expression without parentheses equivalent to each of the following.

22. $(4x)^4$ 23. $(-y^5)^3$ 24. $\left(\dfrac{x}{y^2}\right)^6$

Find each of the following products, quotients, or powers. Express each answer in scientific notation.

25. $(7 \times 10^7)(8 \times 10^8)$
26. $(5)(4 \times 10^5)$
27. $\dfrac{3 \times 10^5}{5 \times 10^1}$
28. $(6 \times 10^4)^3$

Which of these symbols, $>$, $=$, or $<$, should replace ||| in each of the following?

29. $3^2 \cdot 4^2$ ||| 7^2 31. $(2^3)^4$ ||| 2^7
30. $3^2 + 4^2$ ||| 7^2 32. $2^3 \cdot 2^4$ ||| 2^7

Find x in each of the following equations.

33. $5^8 \cdot 5^2 = 5^x$ 36. $\dfrac{12^7}{4^7} = x^7$
34. $8^5 \cdot 2^5 = x^5$
35. $\dfrac{7^{12}}{7^4} = 7^x$

The average distances of Neptune and Venus from the sun are 2.8 billion and 67 million miles respectively.

37. Write each of these distances in scientific notation.
38. How many times farther from the sun is Neptune than Venus?

The following problems are about the exponential function $y = 4(0.5^x)$.

39. Make a table for this function, letting $x = 0$, 1, 2, and 3.
40. Graph the function by plotting the points and connecting them with a smooth curve.

Extra Credit.

How long do you think it would take you to walk one million inches?

8B

ELEMENTARY ALGEBRA
Test on Chapter 8

Name _____

Write each of the following numbers in the form indicated.

1. One hundred billion as a power of ten.
2. The number that is ten times as large as 9×10^5 in scientific notation.
3. The number that is one-tenth as large as 10^{-7} as a power of ten.

Write each of the following numbers in decimal form.

4. 2.5×10^6 5. 8.01×10^{-2}

Write each of the following numbers in scientific notation.

6. $20,000$ 8. 0.017

7. 39×10^8 9. 0.5×10^{-14}

Write each of the following numbers without using any exponents.

10. $(-4)^3$ 12. $(-6)^0$

11. 2^{-5} 13. $(-3)^{-1}$

Write each of the following expressions as a single power of x.

14. $x^{-7} \cdot x^4$ 17. $\dfrac{x^{-12}}{x^{-5}}$

15. $(x^{-7})^4$

16. $\dfrac{x^2}{x^{-8}}$

Which of these symbols, >, =, or <, should replace IIII in each of the following?

18. 10^{-9} IIII 10^{-8} 20. $(-6)^4$ IIII 4^{-6}

19. 3^1 IIII 12^{-1} 21. 5^0 IIII $(-5)^0$

Write an expression without parentheses equivalent to each of the following.

22. $(5x)^3$ 23. $(-y^2)^5$ 24. $\left(\dfrac{x^4}{y}\right)^6$

Find each of the following products, quotients, or powers. Express each answer in scientific notation.

25. $(7 \times 10^7)(9 \times 10^9)$
26. $(4)(5 \times 10^4)$
27. $\dfrac{3 \times 10^6}{6 \times 10^1}$
28. $(5 \times 10^4)^3$

Which of these symbols, >, =, or <, should replace IIII in each of the following?

29. $3^2 \cdot 3^5$ IIII 3^7 31. $2^3 \cdot 5^3$ IIII 7^3
30. $(3^2)^5$ IIII 3^7 32. $2^3 + 5^3$ IIII 7^3

Find x in each of the following equations.

33. $2^4 \cdot 9^4 = x^4$ 36. $\dfrac{6^{15}}{6^3} = 6^x$
34. $4^2 \cdot 4^9 = 4^x$
35. $\dfrac{15^6}{3^6} = x^6$

The average distances of Uranus and Mars from the sun are 1.8 billion and 140 million miles respectively.

37. Write each of these distances in scientific notation.
38. How many times farther from the sun is Uranus than Mars?

The following problems are about the exponential function $y = 0.5(2^x)$.

39. Make a table for this function, letting $x = 0, 1, 2,$ and 3.
40. Graph the function by plotting the points and connecting them with a smooth curve.

Extra Credit.

How long do you think it would take you to walk one million inches?

8C

ELEMENTARY ALGEBRA
Test on Chapter 8

Name _____

Write each of the following numbers in the form indicated.

1. Ten million as a power of ten.
2. The number that is ten times as large as 9×10^8 in scientific notation.
3. The number that is one-tenth as large as 10^{-6} as a power of ten.

Write each of the following numbers in decimal form.

4. 2.5×10^3
5. 8.01×10^{-4}

Write each of the following numbers in scientific notation.

6. $30,000$
7. 39×10^7
8. 0.0017
9. 0.5×10^{-13}

Write each of the following numbers without using any exponents.

10. $(-2)^5$
11. $(-5)^{-1}$
12. 3^{-4}
13. $(-3)^0$

Write each of the following expressions as a single power of x.

14. $x^{-9} \cdot x^5$
15. $(x^{-9})^5$
16. $\dfrac{x^3}{x^{-5}}$
17. $\dfrac{x^{-10}}{x^{-8}}$

Which of these symbols, >, =, or <, should replace ⫿ in each of the following?

18. 10^{-7} ⫿ 10^{-8}
19. 14^{-1} ⫿ 2^1
20. 6^0 ⫿ $(-6)^0$
21. 2^{-7} ⫿ $(-7)^2$

Write an expression without parentheses equivalent to each of the following.

22. $(3x)^5$
23. $(-y^4)^3$
24. $\left(\dfrac{x}{y^6}\right)^2$

Find each of the following products, quotients, or powers. Express each answer in scientific notation.

25. $(8 \times 10^8)(9 \times 10^9)$
26. $(3)(5 \times 10^3)$
27. $\dfrac{2 \times 10^7}{5 \times 10^1}$
28. $(8 \times 10^4)^3$

Which of these symbols, >, =, or <, should replace ⫿ in each of the following?

29. $(3^2)^6$ ⫿ 3^8
30. $3^2 \cdot 3^6$ ⫿ 3^8
31. $2^3 + 6^3$ ⫿ 8^3
32. $2^3 \cdot 6^3$ ⫿ 8^3

Find x in each of the following equations.

33. $4^2 \cdot 5^2 = x^2$
34. $2^4 \cdot 2^5 = 2^x$
35. $\dfrac{9^8}{9^2} = 9^x$
36. $\dfrac{8^9}{2^9} = x^9$

The average distances of Neptune and Mercury from the sun are 2.8 billion and 36 million miles respectively.

37. Write each of these distances in scientific notation.
38. How many times farther from the sun is Neptune than Mercury?

The following problems are about the exponential function $y = 10(0.5^x)$.

39. Make a table for this function, letting $x = 0, 1, 2,$ and 3.
40. Graph the function by plotting the points and connecting them with a smooth curve.

Extra Credit.

How long do you think it would take you to walk one million inches?

8D

ELEMENTARY ALGEBRA
Test on Chapter 9

Name _____

Find the values of the following polynomials as indicated.

$$2x^5 - 5x^2$$

1. for $x = 2$
2. for $x = 3$

$$x^4 + 2x^2 + 1$$

3. for $x = 1$
4. for $x = 10$

If possible, write each of the following as a monomial. If an expression cannot be written as a monomial, say so.

5. $3x^4 + 3x$
6. $6x^5 - x^5$
7. $(-5x^3)^2$
8. $2(-5x^3)$
9. $-5x(x^3)$
10. $2(-5x)^3$

Make a diagram to illustrate each of these products. Then use the diagrams to write each one as a sum of monomials.

11. $(x - 11y)(x + 11y)$

12. $(x + 5)(2y - 3)$

Write each of the following as a polynomial in descending powers of its variable.

13. $5x(x + 4)$

14. $(5x + 1)(x + 4)$

15. $(x + 9)(x - 8)$

16. $(3x - 2)^2$

17. $(x + 7)(x - 7)$

18. $(x^5 + x)^2$

Perform the operations indicated.

19. Add $3x - 7y$, $2x + y$, and $y - 4x$.
20. Subtract $4x^2 - 1$ from $5x^2 - 9x$.
21. Multiply $x + 3$ by $x^2 - 3x + 9$.
22. Divide $x - 6$ into $x^3 + x^2 - 50x + 48$.

Find expressions for the perimeter and area of each of these rectangles.

23. Perimeter of first rectangle.
24. Area of first rectangle.
25. Perimeter of second rectangle.
26. Area of second rectangle.

Find the missing term in each of the following, given that each is the square of a binomial.

27. $x^2 + \text{||||} + 64$
28. $25x^2 - 30x + \text{||||}$

Perform the operations indicated.

29. $(3x^2 - 12) + (x + 2)$

30. $(3x^2 - 12) - (x + 2)$

31. $(3x^2 - 12)(x + 2)$

32. $\dfrac{3x^2 - 12}{x + 2}$

Extra Credit.

Express $(x + 1)^5$ as a polynomial in descending powers of its variable.

ELEMENTARY ALGEBRA
Test on Chapter 9

Name_____

Find the values of the following polynomials as indicated.

$$5x^2 + 2x^3$$

1. for $x = 2$
2. for $x = 10$

$$x^3 - 3x^2 + 3x - 1$$

3. for $x = 1$
4. for $x = 4$

If possible, write each of the following as a monomial. If an expression cannot be written as a monomial, say so.

5. $5x^6 - x^6$

6. $4x^3 + 4x$

7. $2(-4x^3)$

8. $(-4x^3)^2$

9. $2(-4x)^3$

10. $-4x(x^3)$

Make a diagram to illustrate each of these products. Then use the diagrams to write each one as a sum of monomials.

11. $(x + 9y)(x - 9y)$

12. $(2x + 3)(y - 4)$

Write each of the following as a polynomial in descending powers of its variable.

13. $7x(x + 3)$

14. $(7x + 1)(x + 3)$

15. $(x - 6)(x + 9)$

16. $(5x - 1)^2$

17. $(x - 4)(x + 4)$

18. $(x^2 + x)^2$

Perform the operations indicated.

19. Add $5x - 2y$, $4x + y$, and $y - 6x$.

20. Subtract $3x^2 - 5$ from $4x^2 - 10x$.

21. Multiply $x + 4$ by $x^2 - 4x + 16$.

22. Divide $x - 7$ into $x^3 + x^2 - 60x + 28$.

Find expressions for the perimeter and area of each of these rectangles.

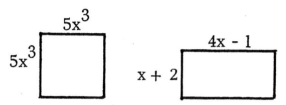

23. Perimeter of first rectangle.
24. Area of first rectangle.
25. Perimeter of second rectangle.
26. Area of second rectangle.

Find the missing term in each of the following, given that each is the square of a binomial.

27. $x^2 + \text{IIII} + 121$

28. $49x^2 - 28x + \text{IIII}$

Perform the operations indicated.

29. $(12x^2 - 3) + (2x + 1)$

30. $(12x^2 - 3) - (2x + 1)$

31. $(12x^2 - 3)(2x + 1)$

32. $\dfrac{12x^2 - 3}{2x + 1}$

Extra Credit.

Express $(x + 3)^4$ as a polynomial in descending powers of its variable.

9B

ELEMENTARY ALGEBRA
Test on Chapter 9

Name _____

Find the values of the following polynomials as indicated.

$$2x^5 + 5x^2$$

1. for $x = 1$
2. for $x = 4$

$$x^4 - 2x^2 + 1$$

3. for $x = 2$
4. for $x = 10$

If possible, write each of the following as a monomial. If an expression cannot be written as a monomial, say so.

5. $(-3x^5)^2$
6. $2(-3x^5)$
7. $-3x(x^5)$
8. $2(-3x)^5$
9. $8x^3 + 8x$
10. $7x^4 - x^4$

Make a diagram to illustrate each of these products. Then use the diagrams to write each one as a sum of monomials.

11. $(8x + y)(8x - y)$
12. $(x - 4)(3y + 2)$

Write each of the following as a polynomial in descending powers of its variable.

13. $4x(x + 6)$
14. $(4x + 1)(x + 6)$
15. $(x + 8)(x - 7)$
16. $(x + 3)(x - 3)$
17. $(2x - 5)^2$
18. $(x^4 + x)^2$

Perform the operations indicated.

19. Add $6x - 4y$, $5x + y$, and $y - 3x$.
20. Subtract $2x^2 - 7$ from $3x^2 - 8x$.
21. Multiply $x + 2$ by $x^2 - 2x + 4$.
22. Divide $x - 3$ into $x^3 + x^2 - 30x + 54$.

Find expressions for the perimeter and area of each of these rectangles.

23. Perimeter of first rectangle.
24. Area of first rectangle.
25. Perimeter of second rectangle.
26. Area of second rectangle.

Find the missing term in each of the following, given that each is the square of a binomial.

27. $x^2 + \text{IIII} + 81$
28. $36x^2 - 48x + \text{IIII}$

Perform the operations indicated.

29. $(2x^2 - 18) + (x + 3)$
30. $(2x^2 - 18) - (x + 3)$
31. $(2x^2 - 18)(x + 3)$
32. $\dfrac{2x^2 - 18}{x + 3}$

Extra Credit.

Express $(x + 5)^4$ as a polynomial in descending powers of its variable.

ELEMENTARY ALGEBRA
Test on Chapter 9

Name_____

Find the values of the following polynomials as indicated.

$$7x^2 - 2x^3$$

1. for $x = 2$
2. for $x = 3$

$$x^3 + 3x^2 + 3x + 1$$

3. for $x = 1$
4. for $x = 10$

If possible, write each of the following as a monomial. If an expression cannot be written as a monomial, say so.

5. $2(-5x^4)$
6. $(-5x^4)^2$
7. $2(-5x)^4$
8. $-5x(x^4)$
9. $8x^3 - x^3$
10. $6x^2 + 6x$

Make a diagram to illustrate each of these products. Then use the diagrams to write each one as a sum of monomials.

11. $(12x - y)(12x + y)$

12. $(3x + 2)(y - 5)$

Write each of the following as a polynomial in descending powers of its variable.

13. $9x(x + 2)$

14. $(9x + 1)(x + 2)$

15. $(x - 7)(x + 9)$

16. $(x - 5)(x + 5)$

17. $(4x - 1)^2$

18. $(x^3 + x)^2$

Perform the operations indicated.

19. Add $4x - 3y$, $7x + y$, and $y - 5x$.
20. Subtract $5x^2 - 2$ from $6x^2 - 4x$.
21. Multiply $x + 5$ by $x^2 - 5x + 25$.
22. Divide $x - 8$ into $x^3 + x^2 - 80x + 64$.

Find expressions for the perimeter and area of each of these rectangles.

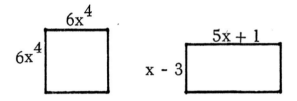

23. Perimeter of first rectangle.
24. Area of first rectangle.
25. Perimeter of second rectangle.
26. Area of second rectangle.

Find the missing term in each of the following, given that each is the square of a binomial.

27. $x^2 + \text{||||} + 49$
28. $4x^2 - 24x + \text{||||}$

Perform the operations indicated.

29. $(18x^2 - 2) + (3x + 1)$

30. $(18x^2 - 2) - (3x + 1)$

31. $(18x^2 - 2)(3x + 1)$

32. $\dfrac{18x^2 - 2}{3x + 1}$

Extra Credit.

Express $(x + 2)^5$ as a polynomial in descending powers of its variable.

9D

ELEMENTARY ALGEBRA
Test on Chapter 10

Name _____

Factor each of the following numbers into primes. List the prime factors in order from smallest to largest, using exponents where possible.

1. 168

2. 475

3. 517

4. 26^4

Find the greatest common factor of each of the following sets of numbers.

5. 92 and 138

6. 4, 6, and 12

7. 6^2 and 6^3

8. 2^6 and 3^6

List all the factors that are positive integers or have positive integral coefficients for each of the following.

9. x^4

10. 21x

Find the greatest common factor for each of the following sets of monomials.

11. 8x and 12x

12. x^8 and x^{12}

13. $27x^2$ and $18y^2$

14. x^3y, x^2y^2, and xy^3

Find the missing term in each of these trinomial squares.

15. $4x^2 - 12x +$ ||||

16. $36x^2 +$ |||| $+ 25$

What should replace |||| in each of the following equations?

17. $(3x^3)($ |||| $) = 9x^9$

18. $2x^6 + 2x = (2x)($ |||| $)$

19. $x^2 - 11x + 30 = ($ |||| $)(x - 5)$

20. $($ |||| $)(2x - 9) = 4x^2 - 81$

21. $48x^2 + 7x - 3 = (3x + 1)($ |||| $)$

Factor each of the following polynomials as completely as possible.

22. $12x - 21$

23. $x + 8x^2$

24. $x^2 - 25$

25. $x^2 + 21x + 38$

26. $9x^3 - 90x^2$

27. $25x^2 + 60x + 36$

28. $x^2 - 5x - 36$

29. $2x^2 + 19x + 42$

30. $3x^2 - 6x + 3$

31. $2x^3 + 18x$

32. $x^3 - 64x$

33. $x^2 + 6xy - 7y^2$

34. $xy - 2x + 5y - 10$

35. $xy^2 - x$

Extra Credit.

Factor $x^3 + 27$ as the product of a binomial and a trinomial.

ELEMENTARY ALGEBRA
Test on Chapter 10

Name _____

Factor each of the following numbers into primes. List the prime factors in order from smallest to largest, using exponents where possible.

1. 294

2. 325

3. 803

4. 39^3

Find the greatest common factor of each of the following sets of numbers.

5. 68 and 102

6. 6, 9, and 18

7. 3^5 and 4^5

8. 5^3 and 5^4

List all the factors that are positive integers or have positive integral coefficients for each of the following.

9. x^3

10. $22x$

Find the greatest common factor for each of the following sets of monomials.

11. $9x$ and $12x$

12. x^9 and x^{12}

13. $15x^2$ and $20y^2$

14. x^2y^2, x^3y, and x^4

Find the missing term in each of these trinomial squares.

15. $25x^2 - 20x +$ ▦

16. $49x^2 +$ ▦ $+ 16$

What should replace ▦ in each of the following equations?

17. $(2x^2)(\text{▦}) = 8x^8$

18. $3x^5 - 3x = (3x)(\text{▦})$

19. $x^2 - 11x + 28 = (\text{▦})(x - 4)$

20. $(\text{▦})(5x - 8) = 25x^2 - 64$

21. $54x^2 + 3x - 5 = (3x + 1)(\text{▦})$

Factor each of the following polynomials as completely as possible.

22. $14x - 21$

23. $x^2 - 36$

24. $x + 5x^2$

25. $x^2 + 20x + 51$

26. $16x^2 - 56x + 49$

27. $25x^3 - 100x^2$

28. $3x^2 - 12x + 12$

29. $x^2 - 4x - 45$

30. $2x^2 + 21x + 27$

31. $x^3 - 16x$

32. $5x^3 + 20x$

33. $x^2 + 4xy - 5y^2$

34. $xy^2 + 2xy + x$

35. $xy - 3x + 2y - 6$

Extra Credit.

Factor $x^3 + 64$ as the product of a binomial and a trinomial.

ELEMENTARY ALGEBRA
Test on Chapter 10

Name_____

Factor each of the following numbers into primes. List the prime factors in order from smallest to largest, using exponents where possible.

1. 156
2. 425
3. 583
4. 21^3

Find the greatest common factor of each of the following sets of numbers.

5. 52 and 78
6. 10, 15, and 30
7. 7^3 and 7^4
8. 3^7 and 4^7

List all the factors that are positive integers or have positive integral coefficients for each of the following.

9. $35x$
10. x^4

Find the greatest common factor for each of the following sets of monomials.

11. $6x$ and $10x$
12. x^6 and x^{10}
13. $8x^2$ and $24y^2$
14. x^2y^2, xy^3, and y^4

Find the missing term in each of these trinomial squares.

15. $16x^2 - 8x + ||||$
16. $64x^2 + |||| + 9$

What should replace |||| in each of the following equations?

17. $(5x^5)(||||) = 10x^{10}$
18. $4x^4 - 4x = (4x)(||||)$
19. $x^2 - 12x + 27 = (||||)(x - 3)$
20. $(||||)(3x - 7) = 9x^2 - 49$
21. $36x^2 - 3x - 5 = (3x + 1)(||||)$

Factor each of the following polynomials as completely as possible.

22. $12x + 22$
23. $x - 4x^2$
24. $x^2 - 64$
25. $x^2 + 18x + 65$
26. $16x^3 - 80x^2$
27. $4x^2 - 36x + 81$
28. $x^3 - 36x$
29. $x^2 - 9x - 36$
30. $2x^2 + 21x + 40$
31. $5x^2 - 10x + 5$
32. $3x^3 + 12x$
33. $x^2 - xy - 2y^2$
34. $x^2y - y$
35. $xy - 5x + 3y - 15$

Extra Credit.

Factor $x^3 - 27$ as the product of a binomial and a trinomial.

10C

ELEMENTARY ALGEBRA
Test on Chapter 10

Name _____

Factor each of the following numbers into primes. List the prime factors in order from smallest to largest, using exponents where possible.

1. 126
2. 575
3. 737
4. 35^4

Find the greatest common factor of each of the following sets of numbers.

5. 76 and 114
6. 14, 21, and 42
7. 2^4 and 5^4
8. 4^2 and 4^5

List all the factors that are positive integers or have positive integral coefficients for each of the following.

9. 26x
10. x^3

Find the greatest common factor for each of the following sets of monomials.

11. 10x and 15x
12. x^{10} and x^{15}
13. $21x^2$ and $14y^2$
14. $2y^3$, $4y^2$, and 6y

Find the missing term in each of these trinomial squares.

15. $9x^2 - 6x +$ ||||
16. $25x^2 +$ |||| $+ 64$

What should replace |||| in each of the following equations?

17. $(4x^4)($ |||| $) = 8x^8$
18. $5x^3 + 5x = (5x)($ |||| $)$
19. $x^2 - 14x + 24 = ($ |||| $)(x - 2)$
20. $($ |||| $)(4x - 5) = 16x^2 - 25$
21. $42x^2 + 5x - 3 = (3x + 1)($ |||| $)$

Factor each of the following polynomials as completely as possible.

22. $15x + 24$
23. $x^2 - 81$
24. $x - 6x^2$
25. $x^2 + 18x + 77$
26. $9x^2 + 30x + 25$
27. $4x^3 - 64x^2$
28. $x^2 - 5x - 24$
29. $2x^2 - 12x + 18$
30. $7x^3 + 7x$
31. $2x^2 + 19x + 45$
32. $x^3 - 100x$
33. $x^2 - 2xy - 3y^2$
34. $xy - 2x + 7y - 14$
35. $x^2y + 2xy + y$

Extra Credit.

Factor $x^3 - 64$ as the product of a binomial and a trinomial.

ELEMENTARY ALGEBRA
Test on Chapter 11

Name_____

Express the answer to each of the following questions in simplest terms.

1. What fraction of this figure is shaded?
2. What fraction is not shaded?
3. What is the sum of these two fractions?

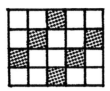

Tell whether or not each of the following equations is true for all allowable values of the variables.

4. $\dfrac{5x}{5y} = \dfrac{x}{y}$

5. $\dfrac{2x + 8}{2x} = 8$

6. $\dfrac{x - y}{x + y} = -1$

7. $\dfrac{x^2 - 9}{x - 3} = x + 3$

If the denominator of a fraction is zero, the fraction is meaningless. What value(s) of x would make the denominator of each of these fractions equal to zero?

8. $\dfrac{x - 2}{x + 7}$

9. $\dfrac{3}{x(x - 4)}$

If possible, reduce each of these fractions.

10. $\dfrac{x^6}{6x}$

11. $\dfrac{3x + 8y}{3x - 8y}$

12. $\dfrac{5x - 5y}{x^2 - y^2}$

13. $\dfrac{xy - 2}{2 - xy}$

Which of the following fractions is larger?

14. $\dfrac{132}{145}$ or $\dfrac{131}{146}$

Write each of the following sums or differences as a fraction in simplest terms.

15. $\dfrac{7}{2x} + \dfrac{1}{2x}$

16. $\dfrac{x}{3} - \dfrac{x + 6}{6}$

17. $x + \dfrac{x^2}{2}$

18. $x + 5 - \dfrac{10x}{x + 5}$

Change each of the following to the form described.

19. Write $\dfrac{x - 8}{x - 4}$ as the difference of two fractions.

20. Write $\dfrac{x^2 + 2x + 2}{x + 1}$ as the sum of an integer and a fraction.

Write each of the following products as a fraction in simplest terms.

21. $\dfrac{x^4}{4} \cdot \dfrac{6}{x^6}$

22. $\dfrac{x}{x - 2} \cdot \dfrac{2 - x}{2}$

23. $(x + 3)^2 \cdot \dfrac{1}{6x}$

Write each of the following quotients as a monomial or fraction in simplest terms.

24. $\dfrac{x^3}{y} \div \dfrac{x}{2y}$

25. $\dfrac{x + 8}{4} \div 2x$

26. $\dfrac{x^2 + 4x - 5}{2x} \div \dfrac{x - 1}{x}$

Simplify.

27. $\dfrac{\dfrac{x}{4} - \dfrac{1}{4}}{x}$

28. $3 + \dfrac{1}{x + \dfrac{1}{3}}$

Extra Credit.

The equation $\dfrac{1}{2}$ ||||| $\dfrac{1}{3} = \dfrac{1}{6}$ is unusual in that ||||| can be replaced by two different symbols of operation to make it true.

1. What are the two symbols?
2. Find another equation of the same type.

11A

ELEMENTARY ALGEBRA
Test on Chapter 11

Name _____

Express the answer to each of the following questions in simplest terms.

1. What fraction of this figure is shaded?
2. What fraction is not shaded?
3. What is the sum of these two fractions?

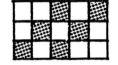

Tell whether or not each of the following equations is true for all allowable values of the variables.

4. $\dfrac{6x}{6y} = \dfrac{x}{y}$

5. $\dfrac{4x + 3}{3} = 4x$

6. $\dfrac{x - y}{y - x} = -1$

7. $\dfrac{x^2}{y^2} = \dfrac{x}{y}$

If the denominator of a fraction is zero, the fraction is meaningless. What value(s) of x would make the denominator of each of these fractions equal to zero?

8. $\dfrac{x - 7}{x + 2}$

9. $\dfrac{1}{x(x - 5)}$

If possible, reduce each of these fractions.

10. $\dfrac{x^7}{7x}$

11. $\dfrac{2x - 6y}{2x + 6y}$

12. $\dfrac{4x + 4y}{x^2 - y^2}$

13. $\dfrac{xy + 2}{xy - 2}$

Which of the following fractions is larger?

14. $\dfrac{132}{145}$ or $\dfrac{133}{144}$

Write each of the following sums or differences as a fraction in simplest terms.

15. $\dfrac{1}{3x} + \dfrac{8}{3x}$

16. $\dfrac{x}{4} - \dfrac{x + 8}{8}$

17. $x - \dfrac{x^3}{3}$

18. $x - 2 + \dfrac{4x}{x - 2}$

Change each of the following to the form described.

19. Write $\dfrac{x - 10}{x - 5}$ as the difference of two fractions.

20. Write $\dfrac{x^2 + 3x + 3}{x + 1}$ as the sum of an integer and a fraction.

Write each of the following products as a fraction in simplest terms.

21. $\dfrac{x^6}{6} \cdot \dfrac{4}{x^4}$

22. $\dfrac{2}{x - 2} \cdot \dfrac{2 - x}{x}$

23. $(x + 5)^2 \cdot \dfrac{1}{10x}$

Write each of the following quotients as a monomial or fraction in simplest terms.

24. $\dfrac{x^4}{y} \div \dfrac{x}{3y}$

25. $\dfrac{x + 12}{6} \div 2x$

26. $\dfrac{x^2 + 6x - 7}{2x} \div \dfrac{x - 1}{x}$

Simplify.

27. $\dfrac{\dfrac{x}{5} + \dfrac{1}{5}}{x}$

28. $4 + \dfrac{1}{x + \dfrac{1}{4}}$

Extra Credit.

The equation $\dfrac{1}{2}$ ▦ $\dfrac{1}{3} = \dfrac{1}{6}$ is unusual in that ▦ can be replaced by two different symbols of operation to make it true.

1. What are the two symbols?
2. Find another equation of the same type.

11B

ELEMENTARY ALGEBRA
Test on Chapter 11

Name_____

Express the answer to each of the following questions in simplest terms.

1. What fraction of this figure is shaded?
2. What fraction is not shaded?
3. What is the sum of these two fractions?

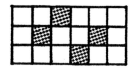

Tell whether or not each of the following equations is true for all allowable values of the variables.

4. $\dfrac{x + 5}{y + 5} = \dfrac{x}{y}$

5. $\dfrac{4x - 2y}{2x} = \dfrac{2x - y}{x}$

6. $\dfrac{-x}{y} = \dfrac{x}{-y}$

7. $\dfrac{x^2 + 9}{x + 3} = x + 3$

If the denominator of a fraction is zero, the fraction is meaningless. What value(s) of x would make the denominator of each of these fractions equal to zero?

8. $\dfrac{x + 2}{x - 7}$

9. $\dfrac{4}{x(x + 3)}$

If possible, reduce each of these fractions.

10. $\dfrac{5x}{x^5}$

11. $\dfrac{4x + 8y}{4x - 8y}$

12. $\dfrac{x^2 - y^2}{3x - 3y}$

13. $\dfrac{2 - xy}{2 + xy}$

Which of the following fractions is larger?

14. $\dfrac{134}{143}$ or $\dfrac{133}{144}$

Write each of the following sums or differences as a fraction in simplest terms.

15. $\dfrac{9}{2x} + \dfrac{1}{2x}$

16. $\dfrac{x}{3} - \dfrac{x - 6}{6}$

17. $x - \dfrac{x^2}{2}$

18. $x - 4 + \dfrac{8x}{x - 4}$

Change each of the following to the form described.

19. Write $\dfrac{x - 12}{x - 6}$ as the difference of two fractions.

20. Write $\dfrac{x^2 + 4x + 4}{x + 1}$ as the sum of an integer and a fraction.

Write each of the following products as a fraction in simplest terms.

21. $\dfrac{4}{x^4} \cdot \dfrac{x^{10}}{10}$

22. $\dfrac{x}{x - 3} \cdot \dfrac{3 - x}{3}$

23. $(x + 6)^2 \cdot \dfrac{1}{12x}$

Write each of the following quotients as a monomial or fraction in simplest terms.

24. $\dfrac{x^3}{y} \div \dfrac{x}{3y}$

25. $\dfrac{x + 10}{5} \div 2x$

26. $\dfrac{x^2 + 5x - 6}{2x} \div \dfrac{x - 1}{x}$

Simplify.

27. $\dfrac{\dfrac{x}{5} - \dfrac{1}{5}}{5}$

28. $2 + \dfrac{1}{x + \dfrac{1}{2}}$

Extra Credit.

The equation $\dfrac{1}{2}$ ‖‖ $\dfrac{1}{3} = \dfrac{1}{6}$ is unusual in that ‖‖ can be replaced by two different symbols of operation to make it true.

1. What are the two symbols?
2. Find another equation of the same type.

11C

ELEMENTARY ALGEBRA
Test on Chapter 11

Name_____

Express the answer to each of the following questions in simplest terms.

1. What fraction of this figure is shaded?
2. What fraction is not shaded?
3. What is the sum of these two fractions?

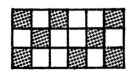

Tell whether or not each of the following equations is true for all allowable values of the variables.

4. $\dfrac{x + 6}{y + 6} = \dfrac{x}{y}$

5. $\dfrac{2x - 6y}{2x} = \dfrac{x - 3y}{x}$

6. $\dfrac{-x}{-y} = -\dfrac{x}{y}$

7. $\dfrac{x^2 - 1}{x - 1} = x + 1$

If the denominator of a fraction is zero, the fraction is meaningless. What value(s) of x would make the denominator of each of these fractions equal to zero?

8. $\dfrac{x + 7}{x - 2}$

9. $\dfrac{1}{x(x + 5)}$

If possible, reduce each of these fractions.

10. $\dfrac{4x}{x^4}$

11. $\dfrac{2x + 5y}{2x - 5y}$

12. $\dfrac{x^2 - y^2}{6x + 6y}$

13. $\dfrac{2 - xy}{xy - 2}$

Which of the following fractions is larger?

14. $\dfrac{134}{143}$ or $\dfrac{135}{142}$

Write each of the following sums or differences as a fraction in simplest terms.

15. $\dfrac{1}{3x} + \dfrac{5}{3x}$

16. $\dfrac{x}{4} - \dfrac{x - 8}{8}$

17. $x + \dfrac{x^3}{3}$

18. $x + 6 - \dfrac{12x}{x + 6}$

Change each of the following to the form described.

19. Write $\dfrac{x - 6}{x - 3}$ as the difference of two fractions.

20. Write $\dfrac{x^2 + 5x + 5}{x + 1}$ as the sum of an integer and a fraction.

Write each of the following products as a fraction in simplest terms.

21. $\dfrac{10}{x^{10}} \cdot \dfrac{x^4}{4}$

22. $\dfrac{3}{x - 3} \cdot \dfrac{3 - x}{x}$

23. $(x + 4)^2 \cdot \dfrac{1}{8x}$

Write each of the following quotients as a monomial or fraction in simplest terms.

24. $\dfrac{x^4}{y} \div \dfrac{x}{2y}$

25. $\dfrac{x + 6}{3} \div 2x$

26. $\dfrac{x^2 + 3x - 4}{2x} \div \dfrac{x - 1}{x}$

Simplify.

27. $\dfrac{\dfrac{x}{4} + \dfrac{1}{4}}{4}$

28. $5 + \dfrac{1}{x + \dfrac{1}{5}}$

Extra Credit.

The equation $\dfrac{1}{2} \; \text{||||} \; \dfrac{1}{3} = \dfrac{1}{6}$ is unusual in that |||| can be replaced by two different symbols of operation to make it true.

1. What are the two symbols?
2. Find another equation of the same type.

ELEMENTARY ALGEBRA
Test on Chapter 12

Name_____

List all of the square roots of these numbers.

1. 81

2. -16

Find an integer equal to each of the following.

3. $\sqrt{34^2 - 16^2}$

4. $\sqrt{34^2} - \sqrt{16^2}$

5. $\sqrt{34^2 \cdot 16^2}$

What symbol, >, =, or <, should replace ⫴ in each of the following?

6. $\sqrt{10} - \sqrt{1}$ ⫴ $\sqrt{9}$

7. $\sqrt{3} \cdot \sqrt{5}$ ⫴ $\sqrt{15}$

Write each of the following expressions in simple radical form. Assume that x > 0.

8. $\sqrt{75}$

9. $\sqrt{700}$

10. $\sqrt{144x}$

11. $\sqrt{x^{144}}$

12. $\sqrt{5x^5}$

Write each of the following expressions as a quotient without a square root in the denominator.

13. $\sqrt{\dfrac{3}{32}}$

14. $\sqrt{\dfrac{7}{x}}$

If possible, simplify the following sums and differences.

15. $\sqrt{98} + \sqrt{2}$

16. $\sqrt{12x} - \sqrt{3x}$

17. $\sqrt{30} + \sqrt{6}$

Simplify.

18. $(4 + \sqrt{5}) + (6 + \sqrt{5})$

19. $(7 + \sqrt{7}) + (28 + \sqrt{28})$

Square as indicated.

20. $(7\sqrt{3})^2$

21. $(1 + \sqrt{10})^2$

22. $(\sqrt{15} - \sqrt{2})^2$

Multiply and simplify.

23. $(\sqrt{3})(\sqrt{15})$

24. $(\sqrt{x^5})(\sqrt{x^7})$

25. $\sqrt{x}(4 - \sqrt{x})$

26. $(2 + \sqrt{6})(5 + \sqrt{6})$

27. $(\sqrt{x} + 3)(\sqrt{x} - 3)$

Rationalize the denominator of each of the following.

28. $\sqrt{\dfrac{25}{4}}$

29. $\dfrac{12}{\sqrt{3}}$

30. $\dfrac{18}{\sqrt{10} - 1}$

Solve the following equations. Simplify radicals where possible.

31. $\sqrt{5}x = 15$

32. $\sqrt{5x} = 15$

33. $\sqrt{5 + x} = 15$

34. $5 + \sqrt{x} = 15$

35. $2\sqrt{x + 1} = \sqrt{x - 5}$

Extra Credit.

Solve for x.

$$\sqrt{x} + \sqrt{x + 6} = 6$$

ELEMENTARY ALGEBRA
Test on Chapter 12

Name _____

List all of the square roots of these numbers.

1. 144 2. -25

Find an integer equal to each of the following.

3. $\sqrt{52^2 - 48^2}$

4. $\sqrt{52^2} - \sqrt{48^2}$

5. $\sqrt{52^2 \cdot 48^2}$

What symbol, >, =, or <, should replace |||| in each of the following?

6. $\sqrt{8} + \sqrt{1}$ |||| $\sqrt{9}$

7. $\sqrt{2} \cdot \sqrt{7}$ |||| $\sqrt{14}$

Write each of the following expressions in simple radical form. Assume that $x > 0$.

8. $\sqrt{300}$ 11. $\sqrt{100x}$

9. $\sqrt{45}$ 12. $\sqrt{5x^3}$

10. $\sqrt{x^{100}}$

Write each of the following expressions as a quotient without a square root in the denominator.

13. $\sqrt{\dfrac{5}{18}}$ 14. $\sqrt{\dfrac{6}{x}}$

If possible, simplify the following sums and differences.

15. $\sqrt{27} + \sqrt{3}$

16. $\sqrt{5} + \sqrt{55}$

17. $\sqrt{24x} - \sqrt{6x}$

Simplify.

18. $(1 + \sqrt{2}) + (3 + \sqrt{2})$

19. $(10 + \sqrt{10}) + (40 + \sqrt{40})$

Square as indicated.

20. $(5\sqrt{3})^2$

21. $(1 + \sqrt{6})^2$

22. $(\sqrt{11} - \sqrt{2})^2$

Multiply and simplify.

23. $(\sqrt{7})(\sqrt{14})$

24. $(\sqrt{x^5})(\sqrt{x^{11}})$

25. $\sqrt{x}(\sqrt{x} - 9)$

26. $(\sqrt{x} + 4)(\sqrt{x} - 4)$

27. $(2 + \sqrt{5})(3 + \sqrt{5})$

Rationalize the denominator of each of the following.

28. $\sqrt{\dfrac{36}{25}}$ 30. $\dfrac{18}{\sqrt{7} - 1}$

29. $\dfrac{15}{\sqrt{3}}$

Solve the following equations. Simplify radicals where possible.

31. $\sqrt{2}x = 12$

32. $\sqrt{2x} = 12$

33. $\sqrt{2 + x} = 12$

34. $2 + \sqrt{x} = 12$

35. $2\sqrt{x + 1} = \sqrt{x - 8}$

Extra Credit.

Solve for x.

$$\sqrt{x} + \sqrt{x + 2} = 2$$

12B

ELEMENTARY ALGEBRA
Test on Chapter 12

Name _____

List all of the square roots of these numbers.

1. 100

2. -49

Find an integer equal to each of the following.

3. $\sqrt{82^2 - 18^2}$

4. $\sqrt{82^2} - \sqrt{18^2}$

5. $\sqrt{82^2 \cdot 18^2}$

What symbol, >, =, or <, should replace |||| in each of the following?

6. $\sqrt{2} \cdot \sqrt{5}$ |||| $\sqrt{10}$

7. $\sqrt{3} + \sqrt{1}$ |||| $\sqrt{4}$

Write each of the following expressions in simple radical form. Assume that x > 0.

8. $\sqrt{99}$

9. $\sqrt{500}$

10. $\sqrt{64x}$

11. $\sqrt{x^{64}}$

12. $\sqrt{3x^3}$

Write each of the following expressions as a quotient without a square root in the denominator.

13. $\sqrt{\dfrac{1}{72}}$

14. $\sqrt{\dfrac{3}{x}}$

If possible, simplify the following sums and differences.

15. $\sqrt{6} + \sqrt{10}$

16. $\sqrt{45} + \sqrt{5}$

17. $\sqrt{8x} - \sqrt{2x}$

Simplify.

18. $(9 + \sqrt{7}) + (5 + \sqrt{7})$

19. $(3 + \sqrt{3}) + (12 + \sqrt{12})$

Square as indicated.

20. $(7\sqrt{2})^2$

21. $(1 + \sqrt{5})^2$

22. $(\sqrt{14} - \sqrt{3})^2$

Multiply and simplify.

23. $(\sqrt{2})(\sqrt{30})$

24. $(\sqrt{x^3})(\sqrt{x^{11}})$

25. $\sqrt{x}(16 - \sqrt{x})$

26. $(\sqrt{x} - 5)(\sqrt{x} + 5)$

27. $(2 + \sqrt{3})(4 + \sqrt{3})$

Rationalize the denominator of each of the following.

28. $\sqrt{\dfrac{25}{9}}$

29. $\dfrac{18}{\sqrt{6}}$

30. $\dfrac{16}{\sqrt{5} - 1}$

Solve the following equations. Simplify radicals where possible.

31. $\sqrt{3}\,x = 15$

32. $\sqrt{3x} = 15$

33. $\sqrt{3 + x} = 15$

34. $3 + \sqrt{x} = 15$

35. $2\sqrt{x - 1} = \sqrt{x + 5}$

Extra Credit.

Solve for x.

$$\sqrt{x} + \sqrt{x + 8} = 8$$

ELEMENTARY ALGEBRA
Test on Chapter 12

Name_____

List all of the square roots of these numbers.

1. 9

2. -64

Find an integer equal to each of the following.

3. $\sqrt{58^2 - 42^2}$

4. $\sqrt{58^2} - \sqrt{42^2}$

5. $\sqrt{58^2 \cdot 42^2}$

What symbol, >, =, or <, should replace |||| in each of the following?

6. $\sqrt{3} \cdot \sqrt{7}$ |||| $\sqrt{21}$

7. $\sqrt{5} - \sqrt{1}$ |||| $\sqrt{4}$

Write each of the following expressions in simple radical form. Assume that $x > 0$.

8. $\sqrt{600}$

11. $\sqrt{36x}$

9. $\sqrt{44}$

12. $\sqrt{3x^5}$

10. $\sqrt{x^{36}}$

Write each of the following expressions as a quotient without a square root in the denominator.

13. $\sqrt{\dfrac{7}{50}}$

14. $\sqrt{\dfrac{2}{x}}$

If possible, simplify the following sums and differences.

15. $\sqrt{10} + \sqrt{15}$

16. $\sqrt{54} + \sqrt{6}$

17. $\sqrt{28x} - \sqrt{7x}$

Simplify.

18. $(5 + \sqrt{3}) + (1 + \sqrt{3})$

19. $(2 + \sqrt{2}) + (8 + \sqrt{8})$

Square as indicated.

20. $(11\sqrt{2})^2$

21. $(1 + \sqrt{7})^2$

22. $(\sqrt{13} - \sqrt{3})^2$

Multiply and simplify.

23. $(\sqrt{5})(\sqrt{10})$

24. $(\sqrt{x^7})(\sqrt{x^{11}})$

25. $\sqrt{x}(\sqrt{x} - 25)$

26. $(2 + \sqrt{7})(3 + \sqrt{7})$

27. $(\sqrt{x} - 1)(\sqrt{x} + 1)$

Rationalize the denominator of each of the following.

28. $\sqrt{\dfrac{25}{16}}$

30. $\dfrac{10}{\sqrt{6} - 1}$

29. $\dfrac{15}{\sqrt{5}}$

Solve the following equations. Simplify radicals where possible.

31. $\sqrt{6}x = 12$

32. $\sqrt{6x} = 12$

33. $\sqrt{6 + x} = 12$

34. $6 + \sqrt{x} = 12$

35. $2\sqrt{x - 1} = \sqrt{x + 8}$

Extra Credit.

Solve for x.

$$\sqrt{x} + \sqrt{x + 4} = 4$$

ELEMENTARY ALGEBRA
Test on Chapter 13

Name _____

Write each of the following equations in standard form. What type of polynomial equation is it and what is the largest number of solutions it might have?

1. $5x^4 = 1 - x^3$

2. $(2x + 7)(x - 2) = 2x^2$

Tell whether or not each of the following numbers is a solution of the equation given.

3. Is 2 a solution of $3x^5 - x = 94$?

4. Is $\sqrt{6}$ a solution of $x^4 = 1,296$?

The graph of the function
$y = x^3 + x^2 - 16x + 4$ is shown here.

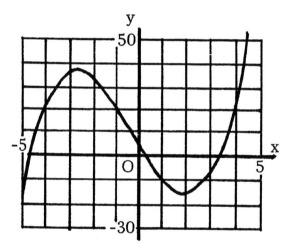

5. Write an equation whose solutions can be estimated from this graph.
6. How many solutions does the equation have?
7. Estimate each of their values to the nearest tenth.

8. Graph the function $y = x^3 - 10$ from $x = -3$ to $x = 3$.

9. Use your graph to estimate the solution(s) of the equation $x^3 - 10 = 0$.

Solve the following equations by the factoring method. Show all work.

10. $2x^2 + 5x - 3 = 0$

11. $(x - 2)(x - 9) = -10$

Solve the following equations by the square-root method. Show all work.

12. $x^2 = 50$

13. $16x^2 + 8x + 1 = 9$

Solve the following equation by completing the square. Show all work.

14. $x^2 - 6x = 1$

Find the value of the discriminant for each of the following equations and use it to tell how many solutions the equation has.

15. $x^2 + 2x + 3 = 0$

16. $3x^2 - 4x - 5 = 0$

Solve the following equations by using the quadratic formula. Show all work.

17. $4x^2 - 7x - 2 = 0$

18. $x^2 - 8x = -11$

Solve the following equations by factoring.

19. $x^3 + x^2 - 6x = 0$

20. $x^4 - 25 = 0$

Extra Credit.

Write the quadratic equation in standard form whose solutions are $1 + \sqrt{5}$ and $1 - \sqrt{5}$.

ELEMENTARY ALGEBRA
Test on Chapter 13

Name_____

Write each of the following equations in standard form. What type of polynomial equation is it and what is the largest number of solutions it might have?

1. $8x^5 = x^2 - 1$

2. $x(x + 3)(x - 3) = 0$

Tell whether or not each of the following numbers is a solution of the equation given.

3. Is 3 a solution of $2x^3 - x = 51$?

4. Is $\sqrt{5}$ a solution of $x^4 = 625$?

The graph of the function
$y = x^3 + x^2 - 16x - 20$ is shown here.

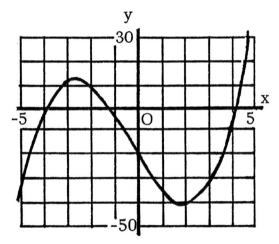

5. Write an equation whose solutions can be estimated from this graph.
6. How many solutions does the equation have?
7. Estimate each of their values to the nearest tenth.

8. Graph the function $y = x^3 + 5$ from $x = -3$ to $x = 3$.

9. Use your graph to estimate the solution(s) of the equation $x^3 + 5 = 0$.

Solve the following equations by the factoring method. Show all work.

10. $3x^2 + 14x - 5 = 0$

11. $(x - 4)(x - 9) = 14$

Solve the following equations by the square-root method. Show all work.

12. $x^2 = 48$

13. $25x^2 + 10x + 1 = 16$

Solve the following equation by completing the square. Show all work.

14. $x^2 - 8x = -9$

Find the value of the discriminant for each of the following equations and use it to tell how many solutions the equation has.

15. $2x^2 + 3x + 1 = 0$

16. $x^2 + 8x + 16 = 0$

Solve the following equations by using the quadratic formula. Show all work.

17. $2x^2 + x - 15 = 0$

18. $x^2 - 4x = -1$

Solve the following equations by factoring.

19. $x^3 - 5x^2 = 6x$

20. $x^4 - 9 = 0$

Extra Credit.

Write the quadratic equation in standard form whose solutions are $1 + \sqrt{7}$ and $1 - \sqrt{7}$.

13B

ELEMENTARY ALGEBRA
Test on Chapter 13

Name _____

Write each of the following equations in standard form. What type of polynomial equation is it and what is the largest number of solutions it might have?

1. $7x^3 = 2 - x^2$

2. $(x^3 + 1)(x + 4) = 4$

Tell whether or not each of the following numbers is a solution of the equation given.

3. Is 2 a solution of $3x^2 - x = 34$?

4. Is $\sqrt{7}$ a solution of $x^4 - 42 = x^2$?

The graph of the function
$y = x^3 + x^2 - 16x - 6$ is shown here.

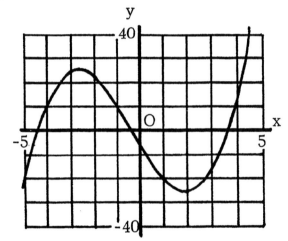

5. Write an equation whose solutions can be estimated from this graph.
6. How many solutions does the equation have?
7. Estimate each of their values to nearest tenth.

8. Graph the function $y = x^3 + 9$ from $x = -3$ to $x = 3$.

9. Use your graph to estimate the solution(s) of the equation $x^3 + 9 = 0$.

Solve the following equations by the factoring method. Show all work.

10. $5x^2 + 9x - 2 = 0$

11. $(x - 5)(x - 4) = 2$

Solve the following equations by the square-root method. Show all work.

12. $x^2 = 45$

13. $9x^2 - 6x + 1 = 25$

Solve the following equation by completing the square. Show all work.

14. $x^2 - 10x = -14$

Find the value of the discriminant for each of the following equations and use it to tell how many solutions the equation has.

15. $x^2 + 6x + 9 = 0$

16. $5x^2 - x - 2 = 0$

Solve the following equations by using the quadratic formula. Show all work.

17. $3x^2 + 5x - 2 = 0$

18. $x^2 - 2x = 5$

Solve the following equations by factoring.

19. $x^3 - 3x^2 = 10x$

20. $x^4 - 36 = 0$

Extra Credit.

Write the quadratic equation in standard form whose solutions are $1 + \sqrt{3}$ and $1 - \sqrt{3}$.

ELEMENTARY ALGEBRA
Test on Chapter 13

Name _____

Write each of the following equations in standard form. What type of polynomial equation is it and what is the largest number of solutions it might have?

1. $6x^2 = x - 2$

2. $(x^2 + 1)(x^3 + 3) = 3$

Tell whether or not each of the following numbers is a solution of the equation given.

3. Is 3 a solution of $3x^2 - x = 78$?

4. Is $\sqrt{6}$ a solution of $x^4 - 30 = x^2$?

The graph of the function
$y = x^3 + x^2 - 16x + 10$ is shown here.

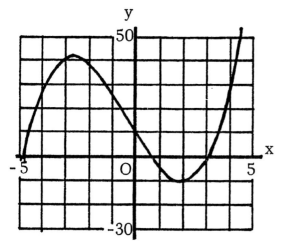

5. Write an equation whose solutions can be estimated from this graph.
6. How many solutions does the equation have?
7. Estimate each of their values to the nearest tenth.

8. Graph the function $y = x^3 - 6$ from $x = -3$ to $x = 3$.

9. Use your graph to estimate the solution(s) of the equation $x^3 - 6 = 0$.

Solve the following equations by the factoring method. Show all work.

10. $3x^2 - 5x - 2 = 0$

11. $(x - 10)(x - 4) = -5$

Solve the following equations by the square-root method. Show all work.

12. $x^2 = 24$

13. $16x^2 - 8x + 1 = 49$

Solve the following equation by completing the square. Show all work.

14. $x^2 - 4x = 2$

Find the value of the discriminant for each of the following equations and use it to tell how many solutions the equation has.

15. $x^2 + 5x + 3 = 0$

16. $4x^2 - 3x + 1 = 0$

Solve the following equations by using the quadratic formula. Show all work.

17. $2x^2 + 9x - 5 = 0$

18. $x^2 - 10x = -23$

Solve the following equations by factoring.

19. $x^3 + 2x^2 = 15x$

20. $x^4 - 4 = 0$

Extra Credit.

Write the quadratic equation in standard form whose solutions are $1 + \sqrt{6}$ and $1 - \sqrt{6}$.

13D

ELEMENTARY ALGEBRA
Test on Chapter 14

Name_____

Tell whether each of the following statements is true or false.
1. Every integer is a real number.
2. The cube root of every integer is irrational.
3. Pi is the number of times that the diameter of a circle goes into its circumference.
4. To every point on a number line, there corresponds a rational number.
5. If the decimal form of a number never ends, it must be irrational.

Change the following rational numbers to decimal form.

6. $\dfrac{3}{16}$
7. $\dfrac{19}{54}$

Write each of the following as the quotient of two integers in lowest terms.

8. $0.\overline{24}$
9. 0.24
10. $1.0\overline{5}$

If possible, find the rational number represented by $\dfrac{4x + 1}{x - 5}$ if

11. $x = 5$
12. $x = 0$
13. $x = 7$

Arrange the following numbers in order from smallest to largest.

14. 0.49, $0.4\overline{9}$, $0.\overline{49}$

List as many of the roots indicated for each of the following numbers as you can. If you think that there are no such roots, write "none."

15. Cube roots of -8.
16. Fourth roots of 625.
17. Fifth roots of 243.
18. Eighth roots of -1.

Which of these symbols, >, =, or <, should replace ‖‖ in each of the following?

19. $\sqrt{10}$ ‖‖ $\sqrt[3]{10}$
20. $\sqrt[5]{-25}$ ‖‖ $\sqrt[5]{15}$
21. $\sqrt[4]{32}$ ‖‖ 2
22. $\sqrt[3]{\dfrac{1}{27}}$ ‖‖ $\sqrt{\dfrac{1}{9}}$

Find exact answers to each of the following.
23. The circumference of a circle whose radius is 4.5.
24. The area of a circle whose radius is $\sqrt{7}$.
25. The radius of a circle whose circumference is 12.
26. The radius of a circle whose area is 45π.

In each of the following problems, let $\pi = 3.14$ and round your answer to the nearest integer.
27. Find the approximate circumference of a wheel if its radius is 8 centimeters.
28. Find the approximate area of the face of a clock if its radius is 5.2 inches.

The following questions are about these numbers: $0.1, \sqrt{2}, -3, \dfrac{1}{4}, 5^0, 0.\overline{6}, 7\pi, \sqrt[3]{8}$.
29. Which ones are counting numbers?
30. Which ones are integers but not counting numbers?
31. Which ones are rational numbers but not integers?
32. Which ones are real numbers but not rational?

Tell whether or not you think the even counting numbers are closed with respect to each of the following operations. If an answer is no, give an example to show why.
33. Addition.
34. Division (excluding zero).
35. Cubing.
36. Subtraction.

Solve each equation below for x and tell what kind of number the solution(s) is.

37. $11x + 4 = 0$
38. $x - \sqrt{7} = \sqrt{28}$
39. $16x^2 - 9 = 0$
40. $\sqrt{x} + 1 = \sqrt{5}$

Extra Credit.

1. Find the decimal form of $\dfrac{1}{98}$ to 12 places.
2. What is interesting about it?

14A

ELEMENTARY ALGEBRA
Test on Chapter 14

Name _____

Tell whether each of the following statements is true or false.
1. Every rational number is an integer.
2. The square roots of most numbers are irrational.
3. If a number is rational, its decimal form never ends.
4. To every point on a number line, there corresponds a real number.
5. Pi is the number of times that the diameter of a circle goes into its circumference.

Change the following rational numbers to decimal form.

6. $\dfrac{13}{40}$

7. $\dfrac{19}{74}$

Write each of the following as the quotient of two integers in lowest terms.

8. 0.48 9. $0.\overline{48}$ 10. $3.0\overline{3}$

If possible, find the rational number represented by $\dfrac{3x + 1}{x - 4}$ if

11. $x = 0$ 12. $x = 4$ 13. $x = 9$

Arrange the following numbers in order from smallest to largest.
14. $0.37,\ 0.3\overline{7},\ 0.\overline{37}$

List as many of the roots indicated for each of the following numbers as you can. If you think that there are no such roots, write "none."
15. Cube roots of -64.
16. Fourth roots of 81.
17. Fifth roots of -32.
18. Seventh roots of 0.

Which of these symbols, >, =, or <, should replace ‖‖ in each of the following?

19. $\sqrt{15}$ ‖‖ $\sqrt[4]{15}$

20. $\sqrt[3]{3}$ ‖‖ $\sqrt[3]{-12}$

21. $\sqrt[5]{-1}$ ‖‖ -1

22. $\sqrt{\dfrac{1}{64}}$ ‖‖ $\sqrt[3]{\dfrac{1}{64}}$

Find exact answers to each of the following.
23. The circumference of a circle whose radius is 5.5.
24. The area of a circle whose radius is $\sqrt{3}$.
25. The radius of a circle whose circumference is 6.
26. The radius of a circle whose area is 28π.

In each of the following problems, let $\pi = 3.14$ and round your answer to the nearest integer.
27. Find the approximate circumference of a wheel if its radius is 14 centimeters.
28. Find the approximate area of the face of a clock if its radius is 6.1 inches.

The following questions are about these numbers: $-1,\ 0.\overline{2},\ 0^3,\ \sqrt{4},\ 0.5,\ 6,\ \sqrt[3]{7},\ \dfrac{1}{8}$.

29. Which ones are counting numbers?
30. Which ones are integers but not counting numbers?
31. Which ones are rational numbers but not integers?
32. Which ones are real numbers but not rational?

Tell whether or not you think the odd integers are closed with respect to each of the following operations. If an answer is no, give an example to show why.
33. Multiplication.   35. Division.
34. Addition.   36. Squaring.

Solve each equation below for x and tell what kind of number the solution(s) is.

37. $6x + 5 = 0$ 39. $9x^2 - 16 = 0$

38. $x - \sqrt{2} = \sqrt{50}$ 40. $\sqrt{x} + 1 = \sqrt{3}$

Extra Credit.
1. Find the decimal form of $\dfrac{1}{98}$ to 12 places.
2. What is interesting about it?

14B

ELEMENTARY ALGEBRA
Test on Chapter 14

Name _____

Tell whether each of the following statements is true or false.
1. Every integer is a rational number.
2. Pi is the number of times that the diameter of a circle goes into its circumference.
3. To every point on a number line, there corresponds a rational number.
4. If the decimal form of a number never ends, it must be irrational.
5. Negative numbers do not have square roots.

Change the following rational numbers to decimal form.
6. $\dfrac{9}{16}$
7. $\dfrac{17}{54}$

Write each of the following as the quotient of two integers in lowest terms.
8. $0.\overline{72}$
9. 0.72
10. $0.0\overline{4}$

If possible, find the rational number represented by $\dfrac{5x + 1}{x - 3}$ if
11. $x = 0$
12. $x = 3$
13. $x = 8$

Arrange the following numbers in order from smallest to largest.
14. 0.58, $0.5\overline{8}$, $0.\overline{58}$

List as many of the roots indicated for each of the following numbers as you can. If you think that there are no such roots, write "none."
15. Cube roots of -27.
16. Fourth roots of 256.
17. Fifth roots of 0.
18. Sixth roots of 1.

Which of these symbols, >, =, or <, should replace ‖‖ in each of the following?
19. $\sqrt[3]{10}$ ‖‖ $\sqrt{10}$
20. $\sqrt[5]{1}$ ‖‖ $\sqrt[6]{1}$
21. $\sqrt[4]{32}$ ‖‖ 3
22. $\sqrt[3]{\dfrac{1}{8}}$ ‖‖ $\sqrt[3]{-8}$

Find exact answers to each of the following.
23. The circumference of a circle whose radius is 3.5.
24. The area of a circle whose radius is $\sqrt{6}$.
25. The radius of a circle whose circumference is 20.
26. The radius of a circle whose area is 52π.

In each of the following problems, let $\pi = 3.14$ and round your answer to the nearest integer.
27. Find the approximate circumference of a wheel if its radius is 12 centimeters.
28. Find the approximate area of the face of a clock if its radius is 7.1 inches.

The following questions are about these numbers: $\sqrt[3]{1}$, -2, 0.3, 4π, $\sqrt{5}$, $\dfrac{1}{6}$, 0^7, $0.\overline{8}$.
29. Which ones are counting numbers?
30. Which ones are integers but not counting numbers?
31. Which ones are rational numbers but not integers?
32. Which ones are real numbers but not rational?

Tell whether or not you think the negative integers are closed with respect to each of the following operations. If an answer is no, give an example to show why.
33. Subtraction.
34. Addition.
35. Multiplication.
36. Cubing.

Solve each equation below for x and tell what kind of number the solution(s) is.
37. $9x + 7 = 0$
38. $x - \sqrt{5} = \sqrt{45}$
39. $4x^2 - 25 = 0$
40. $\sqrt{x} + 1 = \sqrt{6}$

Extra Credit.
1. Find the decimal form of $\dfrac{1}{98}$ to 12 places.
2. What is interesting about it?

14C

ELEMENTARY ALGEBRA
Test on Chapter 14

Name _____

Tell whether each of the following statements is true or false.
1. The square roots of most integers are rational.
2. Negative numbers do not have cube roots.
3. If the decimal form of a number ends, it must be rational.
4. Pi is the number of times that the diameter of a circle goes into its circumference.
5. To every point on a number line, there corresponds a rational number.

Change the following rational numbers to decimal form.

6. $\dfrac{11}{40}$

7. $\dfrac{13}{74}$

Write each of the following as the quotient of two integers in lowest terms.

8. 0.36 9. $0.\overline{36}$ 10. $1.0\overline{8}$

If possible, find the rational number represented by $\dfrac{2x+1}{x-6}$ if

11. $x = 0$ 12. $x = 10$ 13. $x = 6$

Arrange the following numbers in order from smallest to largest.

14. $0.28,\ 0.2\overline{8},\ 0.\overline{28}$

List as many of the roots indicated for each of the following numbers as you can. If you think that there are no such roots, write "none."
15. Cube roots of -125.
16. Fourth roots of -256.
17. Fifth roots of 32.
18. Ninth roots of 1.

Which of these symbols, >, =, or <, should replace |||| in each of the following?

19. $\sqrt{1}$ |||| $\sqrt[4]{1}$

20. $\sqrt[3]{4}$ |||| $\sqrt[3]{-10}$

21. $\sqrt[5]{50}$ |||| 3

22. $\dfrac{1}{27}$ |||| $\sqrt[3]{\dfrac{1}{27}}$

Find exact answers to each of the following.
23. The circumference of a circle whose radius is 6.5.
24. The area of a circle whose radius is $\sqrt{2}$.
25. The radius of a circle whose circumference is 18.
26. The radius of a circle whose area is 40π.

In each of the following problems, let $\pi = 3.14$ and round your answer to the nearest integer.
27. Find the approximate circumference of a wheel if its radius is 13 centimeters.
28. Find the approximate area of the face of a clock if its radius is 4.6 inches.

The following questions are about these numbers: $1^0,\ 2\pi,\ \sqrt[3]{4},\ 0.\overline{5},\ -6,\ \dfrac{1}{7},\ 0.8,\ \sqrt{9}$.
29. Which ones are counting numbers?
30. Which ones are integers but not counting numbers?
31. Which ones are rational numbers but not integers?
32. Which ones are real numbers but not rational?

Tell whether or not you think the positive integers are closed with respect to each of the following operations. If an answer is no, give an example to show why.
33. Subtraction.   35. Addition.
34. Cubing.   36. Division.

Solve each equation below for x and tell what kind of number the solution(s) is.

37. $7x + 3 = 0$ 39. $25x^2 - 4 = 0$

38. $x - \sqrt{6} = \sqrt{54}$ 40. $\sqrt{x} + 1 = \sqrt{7}$

Extra Credit.

1. Find the decimal form of $\dfrac{1}{98}$ to 12 places.
2. What is interesting about it?

14D

ELEMENTARY ALGEBRA
Test on Chapter 15

Name_____

To make 75 pounds of a certain type of concrete, the following ingredients are needed:

       10 pounds of cement,
       15 pounds of sand,
       40 pounds of gravel,
       10 pounds of water.

Give each of the following ratios in simplest terms.

1. The ratio of the number of pounds of cement to the number of pounds of sand.
2. The ratio of the number of pounds of concrete to the number of pounds of gravel.

If possible, simplify the following ratios.

3. $\dfrac{3x^5}{5x^3}$

4. $\dfrac{4x - 4y}{7x - 7y}$

Express each of the following products as a polynomial in simplest form.

5. $18\left(\dfrac{1}{2} + \dfrac{x}{9}\right)$

6. $x\left(4 - \dfrac{5}{x}\right)$

Solve the following equations.

7. $\dfrac{5}{x - 1} = \dfrac{2}{x}$

8. $\dfrac{8}{x} = \dfrac{x}{6}$

9. $\dfrac{1}{5x - 4} = x$

10. $\dfrac{x}{12} + \dfrac{x - 5}{4} = 2$

11. $\dfrac{1}{x} - \dfrac{3}{4} = \dfrac{7}{x}$

12. $\dfrac{5}{x - 4} = \dfrac{10}{2x - 8}$

13. $\dfrac{2}{x} + \dfrac{1}{x + 5} = 1$

The speed that a fish should swim upstream in order to use as little energy as possible is given by the formula

$$v = r + \dfrac{r}{2}$$

in which r represents the speed of the river.

14. At what speed should a fish swim to use as little energy as possible in going upstream in a river flowing 12 miles per hour?
15. Solve the formula for r in terms of v.
16. Use your formula to find r if v = 30.

Solve the following equations for x in terms of the other variables. Simplify your answers as much as possible.

17. $\dfrac{x}{a} - b = 1$

18. $\dfrac{a}{x} + \dfrac{b}{x} = b$

19. $\dfrac{x}{a + 1} = \dfrac{a - 1}{x}$

20. $ax = b - x$

Extra Credit.

If Tom can do a job in 3 hours, Dick can do it in 4 hours, and Harry can do it in 6 hours, how long would it take them working together?

ELEMENTARY ALGEBRA
Test on Chapter 15

To make 45 pounds of a certain type of concrete, the following ingredients are needed:

> 5 pounds of cement,
> 10 pounds of sand,
> 25 pounds of gravel,
> 5 pounds of water.

Give each of the following ratios in simplest terms.

1. The ratio of the number of pounds of cement to the number of pounds of sand.
2. The ratio of the number of pounds of concrete to the number of pounds of gravel.

If possible, simplify the following ratios.

3. $\dfrac{3x^3}{5x^5}$

4. $\dfrac{2x - 2y}{9x - 9y}$

Express each of the following products as a polynomial in simplest form.

5. $15\left(\dfrac{x}{5} + \dfrac{1}{3}\right)$

6. $x\left(\dfrac{2}{x} - 8\right)$

Solve the following equations.

7. $\dfrac{3}{x} = \dfrac{5}{x - 1}$

8. $\dfrac{4}{x} = \dfrac{x}{11}$

9. $\dfrac{1}{7x - 6} = x$

10. $\dfrac{x}{12} + \dfrac{x - 7}{3} = 3$

11. $\dfrac{2}{x} - \dfrac{6}{5} = \dfrac{5}{x}$

12. $\dfrac{4}{x - 3} = \dfrac{8}{2x - 6}$

13. $\dfrac{5}{x} + \dfrac{1}{x + 2} = 1$

The speed that a fish should swim upstream in order to use as little energy as possible is given by the formula

$$v = r + \dfrac{r}{2}$$

in which r represents the speed of the river.

14. At what speed should a fish swim to use as little energy as possible in going upstream in a river flowing 8 miles per hour?
15. Solve the formula for r in terms of v.
16. Use your formula to find r if v = 21.

Solve the following equations for x in terms of the other variables. Simplify your answers as much as possible.

17. $\dfrac{x}{a} + b = 1$

18. $\dfrac{a}{x} - \dfrac{b}{x} = b$

19. $\dfrac{x}{1 - a} = \dfrac{1 + a}{x}$

20. $ax = b + x$

Extra Credit.

If Tom can do a job in 2 hours, Dick can do it in 3 hours, and Harry can do it in 5 hours, how long would it take them working together?

ELEMENTARY ALGEBRA
Test on Chapter 15

To make 95 pounds of a certain type of concrete, the following ingredients are needed:

     10 pounds of cement,
     25 pounds of sand,
     50 pounds of gravel,
     10 pounds of water.

Give each of the following ratios in simplest terms.

1. The ratio of the number of pounds of cement to the number of pounds of sand.
2. The ratio of the number of pounds of concrete to the number of pounds of gravel.

If possible, simplify the following ratios.

3. $\dfrac{2x^7}{7x^2}$

4. $\dfrac{3x - 3y}{5x - 5y}$

Express each of the following products as a polynomial in simplest form.

5. $12\left(\dfrac{1}{6} - \dfrac{x}{2}\right)$

6. $x\left(7 + \dfrac{3}{x}\right)$

Solve the following equations.

7. $\dfrac{7}{x - 1} = \dfrac{4}{x}$

8. $\dfrac{x}{9} = \dfrac{5}{x}$

9. $\dfrac{1}{3x + 2} = x$

10. $\dfrac{x}{12} + \dfrac{x - 7}{4} = 3$

11. $\dfrac{2}{x} - \dfrac{8}{3} = \dfrac{6}{x}$

12. $\dfrac{3}{x - 2} = \dfrac{6}{2x - 4}$

13. $\dfrac{3}{x} + \dfrac{1}{x + 2} = 1$

The speed that a fish should swim upstream in order to use as little energy as possible is given by the formula

$$v = r + \dfrac{r}{2}$$

in which r represents the speed of the river.

14. At what speed should a fish swim to use as little energy as possible in going upstream in a river flowing 10 miles per hour?
15. Solve the formula for r in terms of v.
16. Use your formula to find r if v = 27.

Solve the following equations for x in terms of the other variables. Simplify your answers as much as possible.

17. $\dfrac{x}{b} - a = 1$

18. $\dfrac{a}{x} + \dfrac{b}{x} = a$

19. $\dfrac{x}{b - 1} = \dfrac{b + 1}{x}$

20. $bx = a - x$

Extra Credit.

If Tom can do a job in 3 hours, Dick can do it in 4 hours, and Harry can do it in 5 hours, how long would it take them working together?

ELEMENTARY ALGEBRA
Test on Chapter 15

Name _____

To make 55 pounds of a certain type of concrete, the following ingredients are needed:

> 5 pounds of cement,
> 15 pounds of sand,
> 30 pounds of gravel,
> 5 pounds of water.

Give each of the following ratios in simplest terms.

1. The ratio of the number of pounds of cement to the number of pounds of sand.
2. The ratio of the number of pounds of concrete to the number of pounds of gravel.

If possible, simplify the following ratios.

3. $\dfrac{2x^2}{7x^7}$

4. $\dfrac{5x - 5y}{8x - 8y}$

Express each of the following products as a polynomial in simplest form.

5. $18\left(\dfrac{x}{3} - \dfrac{1}{6}\right)$

6. $x\left(\dfrac{4}{x} + 5\right)$

Solve the following equations.

7. $\dfrac{3}{x} = \dfrac{7}{x - 1}$

8. $\dfrac{x}{5} = \dfrac{8}{x}$

9. $\dfrac{1}{4x + 3} = x$

10. $\dfrac{x}{12} + \dfrac{x - 5}{3} = 3$

11. $\dfrac{1}{x} - \dfrac{10}{7} = \dfrac{6}{x}$

12. $\dfrac{2}{x - 5} = \dfrac{4}{2x - 10}$

13. $\dfrac{4}{x} + \dfrac{1}{x + 3} = 1$

The speed that a fish should swim upstream in order to use as little energy as possible is given by the formula

$$v = r + \dfrac{r}{2}$$

in which r represents the speed of the river.

14. At what speed should a fish swim to use as little energy as possible in going upstream in a river flowing 6 miles per hour?
15. Solve the formula for r in terms of v.
16. Use your formula to find r if v = 24.

Solve the following equations for x in terms of the other variables. Simplify your answers as much as possible.

17. $\dfrac{x}{b} + a = 1$

18. $\dfrac{a}{x} - \dfrac{b}{x} = a$

19. $\dfrac{x}{1 + b} = \dfrac{1 - b}{x}$

20. $bx = a + x$

Extra Credit.

If Tom can do a job in 2 hours, Dick can do it in 4 hours, and Harry can do it in 5 hours, how long would it take them working together?

15D

ELEMENTARY ALGEBRA
Test on Chapter 16

Which of these symbols, =, >, or <, should replace ‖‖ in each of the following?

1. $(-3)^4$ ‖‖ 3^4

2. $\sqrt{50}$ ‖‖ 7

3. $(0.8)^2$ ‖‖ 0.8

4. $-\frac{1}{9}$ ‖‖ $-\frac{1}{10}$

5. $\sqrt[3]{-64}$ ‖‖ -4

Write an inequality in terms of x to represent each of the following figures.

6.
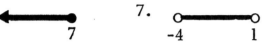
7

7. ○————○
    -4   1

Which of these symbols, =, >, <, ≥, or ≤, should replace ‖‖ in each of the following to make it true for all values of x? If none will, say so.

8. x ‖‖ 10x

9. x - 3 ‖‖ x

10. $\sqrt{x}$ ‖‖ 0

11. x^2 ‖‖ x^3

Which of these symbols, =, >, or <, should replace ‖‖ in each of the following to make it true for all values of the variables? If none will, say so.

12. If a < b and b = c, then a ‖‖ c.

13. If d > e and e > f, then d ‖‖ f.

14. If g > h and h < i, then g ‖‖ i.

Tell whether or not each of the following numbers is a solution of the inequality given.

4x > -20

15. 1   16. -5   17. -2

2x + 9 ≤ 1

18. 0   19. -3   20. -7

Solve each of the following inequalities for x.

21. x - 5 > 30

22. -5x > 30

23. 3x + 8 ≤ -7

24. $9 - \frac{x}{2} < 0$

25. $x \geq \frac{x}{6} + 1$

26. $\frac{-4}{x} < \frac{8}{3}$, if x < 0

27. $\frac{x-2}{3} + \frac{x}{9} < 10$

Solve the following inequalities for x in terms of the other variables.

28. ax - b < 0, if a > 0

29. $\frac{x}{a} > \frac{c}{b}$, if a < 0

30. bx - ax ≤ 1, if b > a

What are the coordinates of the two points on a number line that are

31. 10 units from 6?

32. x units from -3?

Draw a figure to illustrate each of the following equations and inequalities.

33. |x| > 3

34. |x - 6| = 2

35. |x + 2| ≤ 6

Solve for x.

36. |x| + 3 = 5

37. |x + 3| = 5

38. 4|x| = 28

39. |x| - 2 > 9

40. |x - 6| < 0

Extra Credit.

Find all of the solutions of this equation.

|x - 2| + |x - 5| = |x - 8|

16A

ELEMENTARY ALGEBRA
Test on Chapter 16

Which of these symbols, =, >, or <, should replace |||| in each of the following?

1. $\sqrt[3]{100}$ |||| 4

2. 0.9 |||| 0.90

3. |-5| |||| -5

4. $(-1)^6$ |||| $(-1)^8$

5. $-\frac{1}{7}$ |||| $-\frac{1}{14}$

Write an inequality in terms of x to represent each of the following figures.

6.
```
o———————▶
3
```

7.
```
●———————●
-2        7
```

Which of these symbols, =, >, <, ≥, or ≤, should replace |||| in each of the following to make it true for all values of x? If none will, say so.

8. x |||| x + 4

9. 5x |||| x

10. x |||| $\sqrt{x}$

11. x^2 |||| 0

Which of these symbols, =, >, or <, should replace |||| in each of the following to make it true for all values of the variables? If none will, say so.

12. If a > b and b > c, then a |||| c.

13. If d < e and f < e, then d |||| f.

14. If g = h and h = i, then g |||| i.

Tell whether or not each of the following numbers is a solution of the inequality given.

$2x > -18$

15. 0

16. 4

17. -9

$5x + 27 \leq 2$

18. -5

19. 1

20. -4

Solve each of the following inequalities for x.

21. x - 3 < 21

22. -3x < 21

23. 4x + 5 ≥ -7

24. $10 - \frac{x}{6} > 0$

25. $x \leq \frac{x}{4} + 1$

26. $\frac{-5}{x} < \frac{2}{3}$, if x < 0

27. $\frac{x - 8}{2} + \frac{x}{6} > 10$

Solve the following inequalities for x in terms of the other variables.

28. ax + b > 1, if a > 0

29. $\frac{x}{a} < \frac{1}{b}$, if a < 0

30. ax - b ≥ cx, if a > c

What are the coordinates of the two points on a number line that are

31. 12 units from 5?

32. x units from -2?

Draw a figure to illustrate each of the following equations and inequalities.

33. |x| < 7

34. |x - 2| = 6

35. |x + 6| ≥ 2

Solve for x.

36. 7|x| = 42

37. |x| - 5 = 3

38. |x - 5| = 3

39. |x| + 4 > 6

40. |x - 1| ≥ 0

Extra Credit.

Find all of the solutions of this equation.

|x - 1| + |x - 4| = |x - 7|

ELEMENTARY ALGEBRA
Test on Chapter 16

Which of these symbols, =, >, or <, should replace ⦀ in each of the following?

1. $|-1|$ ⦀ -1

2. $\sqrt{80}$ ⦀ 9

3. $(-2)^4$ ⦀ $(-2)^5$

4. $-\dfrac{1}{4}$ ⦀ $-\dfrac{1}{5}$

5. $\sqrt[3]{27}$ ⦀ 3

Write an inequality in terms of x to represent each of the following figures.

6.
-2

7.
3   10

Which of these symbols, =, >, <, ≥, or ≤, should replace ⦀ in each of the following to make it true for all values of x? If none will, say so.

8. $\sqrt{x}$ ⦀ x

9. $(-x)^2$ ⦀ x^2

10. $6x$ ⦀ x

11. $x + 5$ ⦀ x

Which of these symbols, =, >, or <, should replace ⦀ in each of the following to make it true for all values of the variables? If none will, say so.

12. If $a = b$ and $b = c$, then a ⦀ c.

13. If $d < e$ and $e = f$, then d ⦀ f.

14. If $g < h$ and $h < i$, then i ⦀ g.

Tell whether or not each of the following numbers is a solution of the inequality given.

$$3x > -21$$

15. -7 16. 0 17. -5

$$4x + 13 \le 1$$

18. 1 19. -3 20. -2

Solve each of the following inequalities for x.

21. $x - 6 < 24$

22. $-6x < 24$

23. $2x + 7 \ge -11$

24. $8 - \dfrac{x}{3} > 0$

25. $x \le \dfrac{x}{5} + 1$

26. $\dfrac{-2}{x} < \dfrac{6}{7}$, if $x < 0$

27. $\dfrac{x-1}{4} + \dfrac{x}{8} > 5$

Solve the following inequalities for x in terms of the other variables.

28. $ax - b > 1$, if $a > 0$

29. $\dfrac{x}{a} < \dfrac{b}{c}$, if $a < 0$

30. $ax - c \ge bx$, if $a > b$

What are the coordinates of the two points on a number line that are

31. 15 units from 4?
32. x units from -8?

Draw a figure to illustrate each of the following equations and inequalities.

33. $|x| < 1$

34. $|x - 3| = 5$

35. $|x + 5| \ge 3$

Solve for x.

36. $3|x| = 27$

37. $|x| + 2 = 9$

38. $|x + 2| = 9$

39. $|x + 4| \ge 0$

40. $|x| - 5 < 11$

Extra Credit.

Fill all of the solutions of this equation.

$$|x - 2| + |x - 6| = |x - 10|$$

ELEMENTARY ALGEBRA
Test on Chapter 16

Name_____

Which of these symbols, =, >, or <, should replace ⦀ in each of the following?

1. -4 ⦀ $|-4|$

2. $\sqrt[3]{-8}$ ⦀ -2

3. $(-3)^5$ ⦀ $(-3)^4$

4. $-\dfrac{1}{12}$ ⦀ $-\dfrac{1}{6}$

5. 0.70 ⦀ 0.7

Write an inequality in terms of x to represent each of the following figures.

6.
    -4

7.
    $-1 \qquad 6$

Which of these symbols, =, >, <, ≥, or ≤, should replace ⦀ in each of the following to make it true for all values of x? If none will, say so.

8. $|x|$ ⦀ 0

9. x ⦀ $-x$

10. $x - 6$ ⦀ x

11. x^3 ⦀ x

Which of these symbols, =, >, or <, should replace ⦀ in each of the following to make it true for all values of the variables? If none will, say so.

12. If $a = b$ and $b > c$, then a ⦀ c.

13. If $d < e$ and $e < f$, then d ⦀ f.

14. If $g < h$ and $h > i$, then g ⦀ i.

Tell whether or not each of the following numbers is a solution of the inequality given.

$5x > -15$

15. 2 16. -3 17. -6

$3x + 8 \leq 2$

18. 0 19. -2 20. -6

Solve each of the following inequalities for x.

21. $x - 2 > 18$

22. $-2x > 18$

23. $6x + 1 \leq -11$

24. $7 - \dfrac{x}{5} < 0$

25. $x \geq \dfrac{x}{3} + 1$

26. $\dfrac{-8}{x} < \dfrac{6}{5}$, if $x < 0$

27. $\dfrac{x + 4}{2} - \dfrac{x}{10} < 8$

Solve the following inequalities for x in terms of the other variables.

28. $ax + b < 0$, if $a > 0$

29. $\dfrac{x}{b} > \dfrac{a}{c}$, if $b < 0$

30. $ax - bx \leq 1$, if $a > b$

What are the coordinates of the two points on a number line that are

31. 13 units from 7?

32. x units from -4?

Draw a figure to illustrate each of the following equations and inequalities.

33. $|x| > 2$

34. $|x - 5| = 3$

35. $|x + 3| \leq 5$

Solve for x.

36. $|x| - 3 = 2$

37. $|x - 3| = 2$

38. $6|x| = 48$

39. $|x| + 7 < 1$

40. $|x + 5| > 9$

Extra Credit.

Find all of the solutions of this equation.

$$|x - 1| + |x - 5| = |x - 9|$$

16

ELEMENTARY ALGEBRA
Test on Chapter 17

Tell whether each of the following sequences is arithmetic, geometric, or neither. If a sequence is arithmetic, tell the common difference. If it is geometric, tell the common ratio.

1. $7 \quad 7^2 \quad 7^3 \quad 7^4 \quad \ldots$

2. $15 \quad 12 \quad 9 \quad 6 \quad \ldots$

3. $\dfrac{1}{2} \quad \dfrac{1}{3} \quad \dfrac{1}{4} \quad \dfrac{1}{5} \quad \ldots$

What number do you think should replace ⅠⅠⅠⅠ in each of the following sequences?

4. $7 \quad 20 \quad 33 \quad 46 \quad$ ⅠⅠⅠⅠ

5. $-4 \quad 12 \quad -36 \quad 108 \quad$ ⅠⅠⅠⅠ

6. $11 \quad 13 \quad 16 \quad 20 \quad$ ⅠⅠⅠⅠ

7. $5 \quad \sqrt{26} \quad 3\sqrt{3} \quad 2\sqrt{7} \quad$ ⅠⅠⅠⅠ

What number should replace ⅠⅠⅠⅠ in the sequence $\quad 4 \quad$ ⅠⅠⅠ $\quad 36$

8. if it is arithmetic?
9. if it is geometric?

Write the first four terms of the sequences having the following formulas for their nth terms.

10. $t_n = 2 \cdot 4^n$

11. $t_n = 2n^4$

12. $t_n = 3n + 5$

13. $t_n = 7(3 - n)$

14. $t_n = n - \dfrac{1}{n}$

15. Which sequences in problems 10 through 14 are arithmetic?
16. Which sequences in problems 10 through 14 are geometric?

Write a formula for the nth term of each of the following sequences and use it to find the indicated term.

$\quad -4 \quad -3 \quad -2 \quad -1 \quad 0 \quad \ldots$

17. Formula for the nth term.
18. 100th term.

$\quad 4 \quad 16 \quad 64 \quad 256 \quad 1{,}024 \quad \ldots$

19. Formula for the nth term.
20. 6th term.

$\quad -3 \quad -6 \quad -9 \quad -12 \quad -15 \quad \ldots$

21. Formula for the nth term.
22. 25th term.

$\quad 8 \quad 4 \quad \dfrac{8}{3} \quad 2 \quad \dfrac{8}{5} \quad \ldots$

23. Formula for the nth term.
24. 24th term.

Use the formula for the sum of the terms of an arithmetic sequence to find the following sum.

25. $6 + 12 + 18 + 24 + \cdots + 264$

Use the formula for the sum of the terms of an infinite geometric sequence to find the following sum.

26. $135 + 90 + 60 + 40 + \cdots$

Suppose that you get a job for which you are paid $12 the first day, $12.50 the second day, $13 the third day, and so on, with a raise of $0.50 on each successive day.

27. Write a formula for the number of dollars, d, that you would be paid on the nth day.
28. Use the formula to find how much you would be paid on the 30th day.

Suppose that the population of a city doubles every decade and that it is now 17 thousand.

29. Copy and complete the following table.

Number of decades in future:	0	1	2	3
Population in thousands:	17	ⅠⅠⅠⅠ	ⅠⅠⅠⅠ	ⅠⅠⅠⅠ

30. Write a formula for the population in thousands, p, of the city n decades in the future.

Extra Credit.

A ball dropped from a height of 6 feet rebounds on each bounce to a height that is $\dfrac{9}{10}$ of its previous height. How far will the ball travel before it stops?

ELEMENTARY ALGEBRA
Test on Chapter 17

$$\frac{1}{10} \quad \frac{1}{5} \quad \frac{3}{10} \quad \frac{2}{5} \quad \frac{1}{2} \quad \bar{\ } \cdots$$

19. Formula for the nth term.
20. 40th term.

$$-3 \quad -2 \quad -1 \quad 0 \quad 1 \cdots$$

21. Formula for the nth term.
22. 100th term.

$$\sqrt{2} \quad \sqrt{3} \quad 2 \quad \sqrt{5} \quad \sqrt{6} \cdots$$

23. Formula for the nth term.
24. 80th term.

Use the formula for the sum of the terms of an arithmetic sequence to find the following sum.

25. $8 + 16 + 24 + 32 + \cdots + 272$

Use the formula for the sum of the terms of an infinite geometric sequence to find the following sum.

26. $500 + 400 + 320 + 256 + \cdots$

Suppose that you get a job for which you are paid $15 the first day, $15.50 the second day, $16 the third day, and so on, with a raise of $0.50 on each successive day.

27. Write a formula for the number of dollars, d, that you would be paid on the nth day.
28. Use the formula to find how much you would be paid on the 30th day.

Suppose that the population of a city doubles every decade and that it is now 14 thousand.

29. Copy and complete the following table.

Number of decades in future:	0	1	2	3
Population in thousands:	14	‖‖	‖‖	‖‖

30. Write a formula for the population in thousands, p, of the city n decades in the future.

Extra Credit.

A ball dropped from a height of 6 feet rebounds on each bounce to a height that is $\frac{7}{10}$ of its previous height. How far will the ball travel before it stops?

Tell whether each of the following sequences is arithmetic, geometric, or neither. If a sequence is arithmetic, tell the common difference. If it is geometric, tell the common ratio.

1. $1^4 \quad 2^4 \quad 3^4 \quad 4^4 \cdots$

2. $12 \quad 10.5 \quad 9 \quad 7.5 \cdots$

3. $\frac{1}{3} \quad 2 \quad 12 \quad 72 \cdots$

What number do you think should replace ‖‖ in each of the following sequences?

4. $-5 \quad 20 \quad -80 \quad 320 \quad$ ‖‖

5. $6 \quad 18 \quad 30 \quad 42 \quad$ ‖‖

6. $30 \quad 28 \quad 25 \quad 21 \quad$ ‖‖

7. $\frac{1}{2} \quad \frac{7}{12} \quad \frac{2}{3} \quad \frac{3}{4} \quad$ ‖‖

What number should replace ‖‖ in the sequence $\quad 3 \quad$ ‖‖ $\quad 75$

8. if it is arithmetic?
9. if it is geometric?

Write the first four terms of the sequences having the following formulas for their nth terms.

10. $t_n = 2n^3$

11. $t_n = 2 \cdot 3^n$

12. $t_n = 12 - 5n$

13. $t_n = \frac{n}{n+1}$

14. $t_n = 3(n+6)$

15. Which sequences in problems 10 through 14 are arithmetic?
16. Which sequences in problems 10 through 14 are geometric?

Write a formula for the nth term of each of the following sequences and use it to find the indicated term.

$$-2 \quad -4 \quad -6 \quad -8 \quad -10 \cdots$$

17. Formula for the nth term.
18. 15th term.

ELEMENTARY ALGEBRA
Test on Chapter 17

Tell whether each of the following sequences is arithmetic, geometric, or neither. If a sequence is arithmetic, tell the common difference. If it is geometric, tell the common ratio.

1. 7 11 15 19 ...
2. 3^2 4^2 5^2 6^2 ...
3. $\frac{1}{3}$ $\frac{1}{6}$ $\frac{1}{12}$ $\frac{1}{24}$ ...

What number do you think should replace |||| in each of the following sequences?

4. -3 15 -75 375 ||||

5. 34 32 29 25 ||||

6. 2 16 30 44 ||||

7. 16 40 100 250 ||||

What number should replace |||| in the sequence

5 |||| 45

8. if it is arithmetic?
9. if it is geometric?

Write the first four terms of the sequences having the following formulas for their nth terms.

10. $t_n = 2(n + 5)$
11. $t_n = 7 - 3n$
12. $t_n = 4n^3$
13. $t_n = 4 \cdot 3^n$
14. $t_n = \frac{n + 1}{n}$

15. Which sequences in problems 10 through 14 are arithmetic?
16. Which sequences in problems 10 through 14 are geometric?

Write a formula for the nth term of each of the following sequences and use it to find the indicated term.

$\frac{1}{4}$ $\frac{1}{2}$ $\frac{3}{4}$ 1 $\frac{5}{4}$ ...

17. Formula for the nth term.
18. 60th term.

9 10 11 12 13 ...
19. Formula for the nth term.
20. 100th term.

2 4 8 16 32 ...
21. Formula for the nth term.
22. 7th term.

-5 -10 -15 -20 -25 ...
23. Formula for the nth term.
24. 30th term.

Use the formula for the sum of the terms of an arithmetic sequence to find the following sum.
25. $4 + 8 + 12 + 16 + \cdots + 256$

Use the formula for the sum of the terms of an infinite geometric sequence to find the following sum.
26. $128 + 96 + 72 + 54 + \cdots$

Suppose that you get a job for which you are paid $18 the first day, $18.25 the second day, $18.50 the third day, and so on, with a raise of $0.25 on each successive day.
27. Write a formula for the number of dollars, d, that you would be paid on the nth day.
28. Use the formula to find how much you would be paid on the 30th day.

Suppose that the population of a city doubles every decade and that it is now 13 thousand.
29. Copy and complete the following table.

Number of decades in future: 0 1 2 3
Population in thousands: 13 |||| |||| ||||

30. Write a formula for the population in thousands, p, of the city n decades in the future.

Extra Credit.
A ball dropped from a height of 6 feet rebounds on each bounce to a height that is $\frac{8}{10}$ of its previous height. How far will the ball travel before it stops?

ELEMENTARY ALGEBRA
Test on Chapter 17

Tell whether each of the following sequences is arithmetic, geometric, or neither. If a sequence is arithmetic, tell the common difference. If it is geometric, tell the common ratio.

1. $\frac{1}{2}$ $\frac{2}{3}$ $\frac{3}{4}$ $\frac{4}{5}$ ...

2. 8 8^2 8^3 8^4 ...

3. 5.5 9 12.5 16 ...

What number do you think should replace ‖‖ in each of the following sequences?

4. 3 19 35 51 ‖‖

5. -80 40 -20 10 ‖‖

6. 32 31 29 26 ‖‖

7. 1 8 27 64 ‖‖

What number should replace ‖‖ in the sequence 2 ‖‖ 32

8. if it is arithmetic?
9. if it is geometric?

Write the first four terms of the sequences having the following formulas for their nth terms.

10. $t_n = 6 - 2n$
11. $t_n = 3n^4$
12. $t_n = 3 \cdot 4^n$
13. $t_n = 5(n + 1)$
14. $t_n = \frac{n - 1}{n}$

15. Which sequences in problems 10 through 14 are arithmetic?
16. Which sequences in problems 10 through 14 are geometric?

Write a formula for the nth term of each of the following sequences and use it to find the indicated term.

1 $\sqrt{2}$ $\sqrt{3}$ 2 $\sqrt{5}$ ...

17. Formula for the nth term.
18. 100th term.

-4 -8 -12 -16 -20 ...

19. Formula for the nth term.
20. 20th term.

3 $\frac{3}{2}$ 1 $\frac{3}{4}$ $\frac{3}{5}$ ...

21. Formula for the nth term.
22. 15th term.

7 8 9 10 11 ...

23. Formula for the nth term.
24. 40th term.

Use the formula for the sum of the terms of an arithmetic sequence to find the following sum.

25. $7 + 14 + 21 + 28 + \cdots + 273$

Use the formula for the sum of the terms of an infinite geometric sequence to find the following sum.

26. $64 + 48 + 36 + 27 + \cdots$

Suppose that you get a job for which you are paid $20 the first day, $20.25 the second day, $20.50 the third day, and so on, with a raise of $0.25 on each successive day.

27. Write a formula for the number of dollars, d, that you would be paid on the nth day.
28. Use the formula to find how much you would be paid on the 30th day.

Suppose that the population of a city doubles every decade and that it is now 18 thousand.

29. Copy and complete the following table.

Number of decades in future: 0 1 2 3
Population in thousands: 18 ‖‖ ‖‖ ‖‖

30. Write a formula for the population in thousands, p, of the city n decades in the future.

Extra Credit.

A ball dropped from a height of 6 feet rebounds on each bounce to a height that is $\frac{6}{10}$ of its previous height. How far will the ball travel before it stops?

ELEMENTARY
ALGEBRA
MIDYEAR EXAMINATION

1. If someone is x years old now, how old **was** he or she three years ago?
   a) $x + 3$ b) $3 - x$ c) $3x$ d) $x - 3$

2. True or false: These equations are equivalent.
   $$x - 3y = 2$$
   $$2x - 6y = 4$$
   a) True   b) False

3. If the formula $v = \ell wh$ is solved for h, the result is
   a) $h = \dfrac{\ell}{vw}$ b) $h = \dfrac{v}{\ell w}$ c) $h = \dfrac{\ell w}{v}$
   d) $h = \dfrac{w}{\ell v}$ e) $h = \dfrac{\ell v}{w}$

4. The only pairs of positive integers that make the equation $x + 4y = 9$ true are
   a) (1, 2)   b) (1, 5)
   c) (1, 2) and (9, 0)
   d) (1, 5) and (2, 1)
   e) None of these

5. Which one of the following expressions is equivalent to $-(10 - x)$?
   a) $10 + x$ b) $-10 - x$
   c) $-10 + x$ d) $-10 + -x$

6. The decimal form of the rational number $\dfrac{5}{80}$ is
   a) 1.6   b) 16   c) 0.625   d) 0.0625

7. An orchard contains x rows of trees with 12 trees in each row. How many trees are there in all?
   a) $12x$ b) $\dfrac{12}{x}$ c) $\dfrac{x}{12}$

8. The solution of the equation $x - 21 = -9$ is
   a) -12   b) -30   c) 11   d) 189
   e) None of these

9. If $t = 4$ in the formula $v = 120 - 32t$,
   a) $v = 18$ b) $v = 8$ c) $v = -6$
   d) $v = -8$ e) $v = -18$

0. True or false: The product of two numbers is always larger than either number.
   a) True   b) False

1. The value of $x^2 + x - 1$ if $x = -3$ is
   a) -13   b) -7   c) 5   d) 11
   e) None of these

2. The slope of the line $y = x - 5$ is
   a) 1   b) 5   c) -5   d) x

3. The number that is one-tenth as large as 10^{-8} is
   a) 10^{-7} b) 1^{-8} c) $10^{-0.8}$ d) 10^{-9}

4. "The square of a certain number, x, is less than twice the number" written in symbols is
   a) $x^2 > 2x$ b) $x^2 > 2(x^2)$
   c) $x^2 < 2x$ d) $x^2 < 2(x^2)$

5. What must be done to both sides of the equation $4x - 7 = 3x$ to give the equation $x - 7 = 0$?
   a) Subtract 3   b) Subtract 4
   c) Subtract 3x   d) Divide by 4
   e) Divide by 3x

6. The number "107 thousand" written in scientific notation is
   a) 1.07×10^3 b) 107×10^3
   c) 1.07×10^5 d) 1.07×10^6

7. Which one of the following expressions is equivalent to $6(x - 7)$?
   a) $6x - 7$ b) $-36x$ c) $-42x$
   d) $6x - 42$ e) None of these

8. True or false: There is no number equal to $\dfrac{x}{0}$.
   a) True   b) False

9. If the simultaneous equations
   $$12x - y = 27$$
   $$3x + y = 18$$
   are solved, the value of y turns out to be
   a) 1   b) 3   c) 15   d) 21
   e) None of these

0. For this problem, mark "a" on your answer sheet and then graph the function $y = 2^x$ on your graph paper.

MA

1. Which one of the following is equal to $\dfrac{12^5}{4^5}$?
   a) 3^0 b) 3^1 c) 3^5 d) 3^{10}
   e) None of these

2. The equation that results from solving the equation $5x - y = 1$ for x is
   a) $x = 5 + 5y$ b) $x = \dfrac{1+y}{5}$
   c) $x = 5 - 5y$ d) $x = \dfrac{1-y}{5}$
   e) None of these

3. Where does the line $y = -4x$ cross the y-axis?
   a) At 0   b) At 1   c) At -4
   d) None of these

4. The product of -8 and -9 is
   a) -72   b) -17   c) 17   d) 72

5. If a man runs a mile in four minutes, what is his average speed in miles per hour?
   a) $\dfrac{1}{4}$ b) 15   c) 60   d) None of these

6. Which of the following expressions is equivalent to $x + x + x + x + x + x$?
   a) $6x$ b) $6 + x$ c) x^6

7. A formula for the function

x	1	2	3	4	5
y	60	30	20	15	12

   is
   a) $y = x - 60$ b) $y = 60 - x$
   c) $y = 60x$ d) $y = \dfrac{x}{60}$
   e) None of these

8. Which one of the following is equal to 2.1×10^{-3}?
   a) 2.001   b) 21.000   c) 0.021
   d) 0.0021   e) None of these

9. Which one of the following lines has the steepest slope?
   a) $y = 2x + 9$ b) $y = x + 12$
   c) $y = 3x - 1$

0. Which one of the following expressions is equivalent to $3 - (x - 3)$?
   a) x   b) -x   c) x + 6
   d) 6 - x   e) -3x + 9

1. The equation that results from solving $2(y - 5) = x + y$ for y is
   a) $y = x + 5$ b) $y = x + 10$
   c) $y = x - 10$ d) $y = 2x + 10$
   e) $y = 2x - 5$

2. The distance between -6.5 and 1.5 on a number line is
   a) -2.5   b) 3.5   c) 7   d) 9
   e) None of these

3. Which symbol makes the following statement true? $x + 8$ ⦀ $x - -8$
   a) =   b) >   c) <   d) None of these

4. True or false: $(-10)^0 = 1.$
   a) True   b) False

5. Which one of the following numbers can replace x to make this equation true? $2^x = 64$
   a) 5   b) 6   c) 8   d) 16   e) 32

6. A formula for the function

x	0	1	2	3	4
y	4	7	10	13	16

   is
   a) $y = x + 4$ b) $y = 4x$ c) $y = y + 3$
   d) $y = 4x + 3$ e) None of these

7. The expression $x - y$ is equivalent to
   a) $y - x$ b) $-x + y$ c) $x + -y$
   d) None of these

8. Written as a single power, $x^{-3} \cdot x^{-2}$ is
   a) x^6 b) $2x^6$ c) x^{-6} d) $2x^{-5}$
   e) None of these

9. The length marked ? in this figure is
   a) 4   b) x + 8
   c) x - 8
   d) 8 - x
   e) 8 + x

0. For this problem, mark "b" on your answer sheet and then graph the function $y = \dfrac{6}{x}$ on your graph paper.

MB

1. The solution of the equation
   $8 + 5x = 21$ is
   a) 2.6   b) -2.6   c) 5.8   d) -5.8
   e) None of these

2. If gold costs \$300 an ounce, how many ounces can you buy for x dollars?
   a) 300x   b) $\dfrac{300}{x}$ c) $\dfrac{x}{300}$

3. If the simultaneous equations
   $$y + 3x = 19$$
   $$y = x - 1$$
   are solved, the value of y turns out to be
   a) 3.5   b) 4.5   c) 5   d) 8
   e) None of these

4. The sum of -9 and -14 is
   a) -126   b) -5   c) 5   d) 23
   e) None of these

5. True or false: Zero is an integer.
   a) True   b) False

6. Which one of the following is equivalent to $\dfrac{x^8}{x^2}$?
   a) x^4 b) x^{-4} c) x^{-6} d) x^{10}
   e) None of these

7. "Cube x and subtract the result from y" is written in symbols as
   a) $x^2 - y$ b) $y - x^2$
   c) $x^3 - y$ d) $y - x^3$

8. True or false: In an inverse variation, if one variable is doubled, then so is the other.
   a) True   b) False

9. The value of the expression
   $2 + 7 \cdot 8 - 5$ is
   a) 49   b) 27   c) 67   d) 53
   e) None of these

0. The slope of the line through the origin and the point (-3, -6) is
   a) $-\dfrac{1}{2}$ b) $\dfrac{1}{2}$ c) -2   d) 2
   e) None of these

1. Which one of the following figures illustrates $2 \cdot 3^2$?
   a)   b)   c)

   d)   e)

2. The equation that results from adding
   $2x - y = 7$ and $x + 3y = -1$ is
   a) $3x + 2y = 6$ b) $3x - 2y = 6$
   c) $3x + 4y = 6$ d) $3x - 4y = 6$

3. Which one of the following is equivalent to $10x - x$?
   a) 10   b) 9x   c) Neither of these

4. Which symbol makes the following statement true? $(-3)^4$ ||| 4^{-3}
   a) =   b) <   c) >

5. The solution of the equation
   $x + 13 = -1$ is
   a) 12   b) -12   c) -13   d) 14
   e) None of these

6. The value of $(1 - 12)(12 - 1)$ is
   a) 0   b) -120   c) 121   d) -121

7. The equation $7(x + 3) = 3(x + 7)$ has
   a) no solutions   b) one solution
   c) two solutions
   d) infinitely many solutions

8. The equation that results from dividing both sides of the equation $6x - 2y = 8$ by 2 is
   a) $3x - 2y = 4$ b) $3x - y = 8$
   c) $3x - y = 4$

9. True or false: The graph of the equation $y = 4$ is a horizontal line.
   a) True   b) False

0. For this problem, mark "c" on your answer sheet and then graph the equation $3x - 4y = 12$ on your graph paper.

MC

1. The number of the point midway between -7 and 13 on a number line is
   a) 2.5   b) 3   c) 20

2. The solution of the equation $-8x = 20$ is
   a) 12   b) 28   c) -2.5   d) -160
   e) None of these

3. Which symbol makes the following statement true? $(-25)^5$ |||| $(-25)^4$
   a) >   b) =   c) <

4. True or false: One solution of the equation $x^2 - 5y = 21$ is (-1, -4).
   a) True   b) False

5. The value of $x - y^2$ if $x = 3$ and $y = -7$ is
   a) 16   b) 52   c) 100   d) -46
   e) None of these

6. How many hours would it take a car traveling x miles per hour to go 150 miles?
   a) 150x   b) $\dfrac{x}{150}$ c) $\dfrac{150}{x}$

7. True or false: The opposite of every number is negative.
   a) True   b) False

8. Which one of the following is equivalent to $5^4 \cdot 6^4$?
   a) 30^4 b) 30^8 c) 30^{16}

9. How many solutions do the simultaneous equations
   $$2x - 5y = 4$$
   $$2x - 5y = 7$$
   have?
   a) One   b) Two   c) None
   d) Infinitely many

0. Is the eleventh power of 4 odd or even?
   a) It is odd   b) It is even

1. The product of 9×10^9 and 6×10^6, written in scientific notation, is
   a) 5.4×10^{14} b) 54×10^{15}
   c) 5.4×10^{16} d) 5.4×10^{17}
   e) None of these

2. Which one of the following is a solution to these simultaneous equations?
   $$3x + y = 7$$
   $$x = y^2 - 1$$
   a) (-1, 10)   b) (0, 7)   c) (1, 4)
   d) (2, 1)   e) (3, -2)

3. Which one of the following is equivalent to $2(4x^3)$?
   a) $8x^3$ b) $(8x)^3$ c) $8x^6$
   d) $128x$ e) $128x^3$

4. The solution of the equation $15 - 2x = x$ is
   a) -15   b) -5   c) 0   d) 7.5
   e) None of these

5. True or false: The graph of every direct variation is a straight line.
   a) True   b) False

6. A bank contains 30 coins, some of which are dimes and the rest quarters, worth \$5.55. If x is the number of dimes and y is the number of quarters, an equation based upon the numbers of coins is
   a) $10x + 25y = 30$ b) $10x + 25y = 555$
   c) $x + y = 5.55$ d) $x + y = 30$

7. An equation based upon the values of the coins in cents is
   a) $10x + 25y = 30$ b) $10x + 25y = 555$
   c) $x + y = 5.55$ d) $x + y = 30$

8. The number of dimes in the bank is
   a) 10x   b) 7   c) 17   d) 13
   e) None of these

9. Written as a power of 2, $\dfrac{1}{8}$ is
   a) 2^{-4} b) 2^{-3} c) 2^3 d) 8^{-1}
   e) None of these

0. For this problem, mark "d" on your answer sheet and then solve these simultaneous equations by graphing them on your graph paper.
   $$y = 2x - 5$$
   $$x + y = 4$$

MD

ELEMENTARY
ALGEBRA
FINAL EXAMINATION

1. What symbol should replace ‖‖ in -4.1 ‖‖ -4.01?
   a) <   b) =   c) >

2. True or false: The number $\sqrt{121}$ is irrational.
   a) True   b) False

3. If the simultaneous equations
   $$5x + y = 2$$
   $$x = y - 8$$
   are solved, the value of y turns out to be
   a) 7   b) -1   c) 15   d) None of these

4. Find the product: $-2(-4)(-6)$.
   a) 48   b) -48   c) 96   d) -96

5. Write as a quotient without a square root in the denominator: $\sqrt{\dfrac{2}{x}}$.
   a) $\dfrac{\sqrt{2}x}{x}$ b) $\dfrac{\sqrt{2x}}{x}$ c) $\dfrac{2}{\sqrt{2x}}$ d) $\sqrt{\dfrac{2x}{x^2}}$

6. Find the quotient:
   $$x + 6 \overline{)\, x^3 + 4x^2 - 9x + 18\,}$$
   a) $x^2 + 2x + 3$ b) $x^2 + 2x - 3$
   c) $x^2 - 2x + 3$ d) $x^2 - 2x - 3$

7. Divide and simplify: $\dfrac{\sqrt{84}}{\sqrt{7}}$.
   a) $4\sqrt{3}$ b) $\sqrt{12}$ c) $\dfrac{2\sqrt{21}}{\sqrt{7}}$ d) $2\sqrt{3}$

8. Simplify: $\dfrac{2}{\frac{1}{3} - \frac{1}{4}}$.
   a) $\dfrac{1}{6}$ b) $\dfrac{1}{24}$ c) 2   d) -2   e) 24

9. The formulas for the circumference and area of a circle are $c = 2\pi r$ and $a = \pi r^2$. Find the exact area of a circle whose circumference is 10π.
   a) $\sqrt{10}$ b) 25π c) $25\pi^3$
   d) 64π e) $64\pi^3$

0. Solve for x in terms of the other variables: $ax - b = bx$.
   a) $x = \dfrac{1}{a}$ b) $x = \dfrac{b}{a + b}$ c) $x = \dfrac{b}{b - a}$
   d) $x = \dfrac{bx + b}{a}$ e) $x = \dfrac{b}{a - b}$

1. Add $7x + 2y - 6$ and $3x - 2y + 1$.
   a) $10x - 7$ b) $2x - 1$ c) $10x - 5$
   d) $5(x - 1)$ e) None of these

2. Write as a fraction in simplest terms: $\dfrac{x^2}{2} \cdot \dfrac{x^3}{3}$.
   a) $\dfrac{x^5}{5}$ b) $\dfrac{x^5}{6}$ c) $\dfrac{x^6}{6}$ d) $\dfrac{x^2 + x^3}{6}$

3. The cube root of 15 is approximately 2.4662. Round this number to the nearest hundredth.
   a) 2.45   b) 2.450   c) 2.46
   d) 2.47   e) 2.500

4. Write in scientific notation: 186,000.
   a) 1.86×10^3 b) 186×10^3
   c) 1.86×10^5 d) 1.86×10^{-5}

5. Write as a monomial: $(x^6)^3$.
   a) $x^6 + x^6 + x^6$ b) x^9
   c) x^{18} d) x^{216}

6. Factor: $x^2 - 10x + 24$.
   a) $x(x - 10) + 24$ b) $(x + 12)(x - 2)$
   c) $(x - 12)(x + 2)$ d) $(x - 4)(x - 6)$

7. Multiply and simplify: $(x - \sqrt{y})(x + \sqrt{y})$.
   a) $x^2 - \sqrt{y}$ b) $(x^2 - \sqrt{y})^2$
   c) $x^2 - 2x\sqrt{y}$ d) $x^2 - y$

8. Express the perimeter of this rectangle as a polynomial in simplest form.
   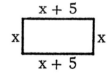
   a) $2x + 5$
   b) $x^2 + 12x + 25$ c) $4x + 10$
   d) $2x + 10 + 2x$ e) $x^4 + 10x^2$

9. Express the area of the rectangle as a polynomial in simplest form.
   a) $x^2 + 5x$ b) $x^4 + 25$ c) $2x + 5x$
   d) $x^4 + 10x^3 + 25x^2$ e) $(x^2 + 5x)^2$

0. Reduce to lowest terms: $\dfrac{2x}{10xy}$.
   a) $\dfrac{1}{5xy}$ b) $5y$ c) $\dfrac{1}{5y}$
   d) $\dfrac{x}{5y}$ e) $\dfrac{x}{5xy}$

FA

1. Find the value of the polynomial $5x^2 - x + 4$ if $x = -3$.
   a) 52   b) -38   c) 61
   d) 46   e) -44

2. Which of these numbers is largest?
   a) $0.51\overline{5}$ b) $0.5\overline{15}$ c) $0.\overline{515}$

3. True or false: $\sqrt{6^2 + 8^2} = 6 + 8$.
   a) True   b) False

4. Write as a fraction in simplest terms:
   $$\frac{x}{6} - \frac{y}{2}.$$
   a) $\dfrac{3y - x}{6}$ b) $\dfrac{x - y}{4}$ c) $\dfrac{2x - 6y}{12}$
   d) $\dfrac{x - 3y}{6}$ e) $2x - 6y$

5. Find the greatest common factor of 42 and 70.
   a) 210   b) 7   c) 14   d) 10
   e) None of these

6. Factor $4x^2 - y^2$.
   a) $4(x - y)(x + y)$ b) $(2x^2 + y)(2x^2 - y)$
   c) $(2x - y)^2$ d) $(2x + y)(2x - y)$

7. Express as an integer: $\sqrt{(-9)^2}$.
   a) -9   b) 3   c) ±9 c) 81   e) 9

8. True or false: The integers are closed with respect to subtraction.
   a) True   b) False

9. Factor as completely as possible: $x^3 - x$.
   a) $x(x^2 - 1)$ b) x^2 c) $x(x^2 - x)$
   d) $x(x + 1)(x - 1)$

0. Solve for x: $4x^2 + 4x + 1 = 25$.
   a) 2   b) -2 and -3   c) -2 and 3
   d) 3 and -3   e) 2 and -3

1. The volume of a cone is given by the formula $v = \dfrac{\pi r^2 h}{3}$. Solve this formula for h in terms of v and r.
   a) $h = \dfrac{v\pi r^2}{3}$ b) $h = 3v - \pi r^2$
   c) $r = \sqrt{\dfrac{3v}{\pi h}}$ d) $h = \dfrac{3v}{\pi r^2}$

2. Solve for x: $\dfrac{5}{x + 1} = \dfrac{10}{x}$.
   a) $-\dfrac{1}{5}$ b) $2x + 2$ c) 5   d) -2
   e) $2x$

3. Solve for x in terms of the other variables: $\dfrac{x - a}{b} = \dfrac{b}{a}$.
   a) $x = \dfrac{b^2 - a^2}{a}$ b) $x = \dfrac{(a - b)(a + b)}{a}$
   c) $x = \dfrac{a^2 + b^2}{a}$ d) $x = b^2 + a$

4. Find the value of $2x - 3y$ if $x = -6$ and $y = -1$.
   a) 9   b) -9   c) -15   d) 15
   e) None of these

5. Factor 198 into primes.
   a) $2 \cdot 9 \cdot 11$ b) $2 \cdot 3^2 \cdot 11$ c) $3\sqrt{22}$
   d) $2^2 \cdot 3 \cdot 11$

6. Find the product: $(x - 1)(x^2 + x + 1)$.
   a) $x^2 - x + 1$ b) $x^3 - 1$
   c) $x^3 + x^2 + x$ d) $x^3 + 1$ e) $x^3 + x$

7. Simplify: $\sqrt{2} + \sqrt{18}$.
   a) $3\sqrt{2}$ b) 6   c) $6\sqrt{2}$
   d) $\sqrt{2} + 3\sqrt{2}$ e) $4\sqrt{2}$

8. Write as a fraction in simplest terms:
   $$\frac{1}{x} + \frac{1}{y}.$$
   a) $\dfrac{xy}{xy}$ b) $\dfrac{2}{x + y}$ c) $\dfrac{1}{xy}$ d) $\dfrac{1}{x + y}$
   e) $\dfrac{x + y}{xy}$

9. Write as a monomial: $(6x)^3$.
   a) $6x^3$ b) $6x^9$ c) $216x$ d) $216x^3$
   e) $216x^9$

0. A hiker walks from a campsite to the top of a mountain at the rate of 2 miles per hour and down again at the rate of 3 miles per hour. The entire hike takes 5 hours. How far is it from the campsite to the top of the mountain?
   a) 1 mile   b) 2 miles   c) 5 miles
   d) 6 miles   e) 10 miles

FB

1. What symbol should replace ⅢⅢ in $\sqrt[3]{20}$ ⅢⅢ $\sqrt[4]{20}$?
   a) $<$ b) $=$ c) $>$

2. Factor: $2x^2 + 5x - 3$.
   a) $x(2x + 5) - 3$ b) -3 and $\frac{1}{2}$
   c) $(2x - 1)(x + 3)$ d) $(2x + 3)(x + 1)$
   e) $-\frac{3}{2}$ and -1

3. Simplify: $8\sqrt{5} - \sqrt{5}$.
   a) $7\sqrt{5}$ b) 8 c) -40
   d) None of these

4. Write as the square of a binomial:
   $$9x^4 - 6x^2 + 1.$$
   a) $3x^2 - 1$ b) $(3x^2 - 1)^2$
   c) $3x^2 - 3x + 1$ d) $(3x^2 - 3x + 1)^2$
   e) $3x^2 - 3x + 2$

5. Find the greatest common factor of $2x^5$ and $5x^2$.
   a) $10x^5$ b) $2x^2$ c) $2x$
   d) x^2 e) 5

6. Reduce to lowest terms: $\dfrac{x + 3}{4x + 12}$.
   a) $\dfrac{1}{8}$ b) 8 c) $\dfrac{1}{4}$ d) $\dfrac{1}{4x + 4}$
   e) Not possible

7. Which fraction is not equal to the others?
   a) $\dfrac{3}{5}$ b) $-\dfrac{3}{5}$ c) $\dfrac{-3}{-5}$ d) $-\dfrac{-3}{5}$

8. Simplify: $\sqrt[4]{\dfrac{1}{10,000}}$.
   a) $\sqrt{\dfrac{1}{10}}$ b) 0.1 c) $\pm\dfrac{1}{10}$
   d) ± 10 e) $\sqrt[4]{1^{-4}}$

9. Solve for x: $x + \sqrt{3} = \sqrt{300}$.
   a) $10\sqrt{3}$ b) $\sqrt{100}$ c) $9\sqrt{3}$
   d) 10 e) $\pm\sqrt{303}$

0. Express as an integer: $\dfrac{x - 2y}{2y - x}$.
   a) 1 b) $\dfrac{x - y}{y - x}$ c) 0 d) $x^2 - 4y^2$
   e) -1

1. Solve for x: $2(5x + 1) = 9(15 - x)$.
   a) 17 b) 133 c) 7 d) None of these

2. Solve for x: $(x - 1)(x + 2) = x^2 + 9$.
   a) 7 b) $\pm\sqrt{7}$ c) ± 3 d) 11 e) -1

3. Solve for x: $\dfrac{x}{4} - 1 = \dfrac{x}{12}$.
   a) 3 b) $\dfrac{3}{2}$ c) 6 d) $\dfrac{4}{3}$

4. Which of these equations does not have any solutions?
   a) $x + 4 = x$ b) $3x = x$ c) $x^2 - x = 0$
   d) All of them   e) None of them

5. Which one of the following properties is illustrated by this equation?
   $$(x + y) + z = x + (y + z)$$
   a) Commutative property
   b) Associative property
   c) Distributive property

6. Write 5^{-3} without using any exponents.
   a) 0.005 b) $\dfrac{1}{0.005}$ c) -125
   d) $\dfrac{1}{125}$ e) 0.0005

7. What value(s) of x would make the denominator of the fraction $\dfrac{x - 4}{x^2 - 9}$ equal to zero?
   a) 3 b) 0 c) 3 and 4 d) 3 and -3

8. Write as a fraction in simplest terms:
   $$\dfrac{3x + 2}{4} + \dfrac{x - 1}{4}.$$
   a) $x - 1$ b) $\dfrac{4x + 1}{4}$ c) $x + 1$
   d) $\dfrac{4x - 1}{4}$ e) $x + \dfrac{1}{4}$

9. Solve for x: $x^2 - 7x + 11 = 0$.
   a) 2 b) $7 \pm \dfrac{\sqrt{5}}{2}$ c) 1 and 6
   d) $\dfrac{7 \pm \sqrt{5}}{2}$ e) None of these

0. Express as a polynomial: $(x + 3y)^2$.
   a) $x^2 + 6xy + y^2$ b) $x^2 + 6xy + 9y^2$
   c) $x^2 + 6xy + 6y$ d) $x^2 + 6xy + 3y^2$
   e) $x^2 + 9y^2$

FC

1. What is the slope of the line having the equation $y = x - 8$?
   a) 1   b) 2   c) 4   d) -8

2. Simplify: $x \div \dfrac{1}{x^5}$.
   a) $\dfrac{1}{x^4}$ b) $\dfrac{1}{x^6}$ c) x^6 d) $\dfrac{x}{x^5}$ e) $\dfrac{x}{x^4}$

3. Factor $15x^2 + x - 2$.
   a) $(3x + 1)(5x - 2)$ b) $(3x + 2)(5x - 1)$
   c) $(5x - 1)(x + 2)$ d) $(3x - 1)(5x + 2)$
   e) $x(15x + 1) - 2$

4. Simplify: $\dfrac{x^2}{x + y} - \dfrac{y^2}{x + y}$.
   a) $x^2 - y^2$ b) $\dfrac{x - y}{x + y}$ c) $\dfrac{x^2 - y^2}{x + y}$
   d) $x - y$ e) 1

5. Multiply and simplify: $\left(x + \dfrac{1}{4}\right)\left(x + \dfrac{3}{4}\right)$.
   a) $x^2 + x + 1$ b) $2x + 1$
   c) $x^2 + x + \dfrac{3}{16}$ d) $4x^2 + 4x + 3$
   e) $x^2 + 4x + 1$

6. Write $\sqrt{x^5}$ in simple radical form.
   a) $2x\sqrt{x}$ b) x^3 c) $x^2\sqrt{x}$
   d) $2.5\sqrt{x}$ e) $2x\sqrt{x^2}$

7. Write as a fraction in simplest terms:
   $$\dfrac{x}{x - 1} \div \dfrac{7}{x - 1}.$$
   a) $\dfrac{x^2 - x}{7x - 7}$ b) $\dfrac{x}{7}$ c) $\dfrac{7x - 7}{x^2 - x}$ d) $\dfrac{x}{7(x - 1)}$

8. Solve for x: $(x - 3)^2 = 7$.
   a) $\dfrac{3 \pm \sqrt{7}}{2}$ b) 4   c) $3 + \sqrt{7}$
   d) $\sqrt{10}$ e) $3 \pm \sqrt{7}$

9. Solve for x: $\sqrt{x + 16} = 2\sqrt{3}$.
   a) 6   b) $4\sqrt{3} - 16$ c) -4   d) 20
   e) -10

0. Simplify: $x^3 \cdot \dfrac{3}{x}$.
   a) x^5 b) $\dfrac{3x^3}{x}$ c) $\dfrac{3x^4}{1}$ d) $3x^2$

1. Multiply: $(5x - 2)(5x + 2)$.
   a) $25x - 4$ b) $25x^2$ c) $25x^2 - 4$

2. What is the degree of the polynomial $7x^2 - x^3 + 10$?
   a) 2   b) 3   c) 7   d) 10

3. Write in simple radical form: $\sqrt{75}$.
   a) 8.66   b) $5\sqrt{3}$ c) $5\sqrt{15}$
   d) $15\sqrt{5}$

4. Between what two consecutive integers does $\dfrac{22}{7}$ lie?
   a) $\dfrac{21}{7}$ and $\dfrac{23}{7}$ b) 2 and 3
   c) 22 and 7   d) None of these

5. Solve for x: $x^2 + 4x = 45$.
   a) $(x + 9)(x - 5)$ b) 9 and -5
   c) $(x + 5)(x - 9)$ d) 5   e) 5 and -9

6. Write as a fraction in simplest terms:
   $$x + 5 + \dfrac{25}{x - 5}$$
   a) $\dfrac{x + 30}{x - 5}$ b) $\dfrac{x^2}{x - 5}$ c) x^2 d) $\dfrac{x}{-5}$
   e) $\dfrac{x^2 - 10x + 50}{x - 5}$

7. What values of x will make the product $6x(x + 4)$ equal to zero?
   a) -4 and -6   b) 2 and -2   c) 0
   d) 0 and -4

8. Factor $9x + 12$.
   a) $3x + 4$ b) $3(3x - 4)$
   c) $(3x + 4)(3 + 3)$ d) $3(3x + 4)$
   e) $3 \cdot 3 \cdot x + 3 \cdot 2 \cdot 2$

9. Find the product $(2x - 9)(x + 4)$.
   a) $2x^2 - 5x - 36$ b) $2x^3 - x - 36$
   c) $2x^2 - 36$ d) $2x^2 - x + 36$
   e) $2x^2 - x - 36$

0. At a hamburger stand, a regular hamburger costs $1.25 and one with cheese costs $1.50. During one day, the stand takes in $205 from the sale of 150 hamburgers. How many regular hamburgers were sold?
   a) 80   b) 14   c) 120   d) None of these

ELEMENTARY
ALGEBRA
WORD PROBLEMS
AND
ADDITIONAL EXERCISES

Note:

The exercises in Elementary Algebra are organized for the most part to afford practice and mastery of specific skills. Practice with a single skill is provided by the lettered parts of a single, numbered exercise. This organization allows students to concentrate on each concept and enables teachers to identify their students' strengths and weaknesses. The text contains more than eleven thousand of these parts, an ample number for learning, practice, and review.

For variety, I frequently assign problems from other sources. Groups of problems of this sort are found in the Teacher's Guide and, in a form suitable for reproduction, in the Transparency Masters. They can be used on the board, with an overhead projector, or as handouts. There are more than sixty such short problem sets in the Guide.

Routine exercises in the text itself are assembled into short groups aimed at strengthening specific skills. Rather than treating word problems as a special topic, I have emphasized the passage from concrete examples and descriptions in words to algebra. Thus, word problems appear throughout Elementary Algebra, instead of being segregated in one or a few lessons.

For teachers who like their students to sit down to a massed group of exercises or word problems, I have included the following pages. You may want to add your own variations, favorite exercises, and helpful ideas.

ELEMENTARY ALGEBRA
Word Problems, Set 1

1. A man distributed 70 cents among four poor persons; giving the second twice, the third three times, and the fourth four times, as much as he gave the first. What did he give to each?

2. A father is seven, and a mother five, times as old as their son; and the difference of their ages is 16 years. How old is the son?

3. A boy bought 2 oranges, 3 pears and 4 apples, for 22 cents. He gave as much for a pear as for 2 apples; and twice as much for an orange, as for a pear and an apple. What was the price of each?

4. What number is that which, being added to 5, and also multiplied by 5, the product shall be 4 times the sum?

5. A gentleman gave to two beggars 67 cents, giving to the second 13 cents less than to the first. How many cents did each receive?

6. A privateer, running at the rate of 10 miles an hour, discovers a ship 18 miles off, making way at the rate of 8 miles an hour. In how many hours will the ship be overtaken?

7. The age of A is double that of B; the age of B is three times that of C; and the sum of their ages is 140. What is the age of each?

8. One man leaves New York for Boston, and travels 9 miles an hour; another man leaves Boston for New York, and travels 7 miles an hour. In how many hours will they meet, the cities being 224 miles apart?

9. A asked B how much money he had; who replied, that if he had seven times as much, he could lend four times what he then had, and have $69 left. How much had he?

0. An express had been travelling 5 days, at the rate of 60 miles a day, when another was dispatched after him, who travelled 75 miles a day. In how many days did the latter overtake the former?

ELEMENTARY ALGEBRA
Word Problems, Set 2

1. A farmer bought a horse, a chaise and a house, for $800. Now, he paid 4 times as much for the chaise as for the horse, and 5 times as much for the house as for the chaise. What was the price of each?

2. Two men, A and B, travel the same way; A at the rate of 45 miles, and B 30 miles, a day. In how many days will they be 300 miles apart?

3. If they were to travel in opposite directions, in how many days would they be 300 miles apart?

4. A father is 40 years old, and his son is 8. In how many years will the father's age be 3 times the son's?

5. A steam-boat has 81 passengers; there being twice as many women as children, and three times as many men as women. What is the number of men, women and children?

6. A courier had been travelling 4 days, at the rate of 6 miles an hour, when another was sent after him, who travelled 8 miles an hour. In how many days will the second courier overtake the first, if they both travel 15 hours a day?

7. Three adventurers, A, B and C, bought 10,170 acres of wild land. By the terms of the contract, B had 549 acres less than A, and C had 987 acres more than B. How many acres had each?

8. A man has six children, whose united ages are 42 years; and the common difference of their ages is equal to the age of the youngest child. What are their several ages?

9. A waterman went down a river and returned again in 6 hours. Now, with the stream, he can row 9 miles an hour; but, against it, he can make a headway of only 3 miles an hour. How far did he go?

10. A father gives to his six sons $2,010, which they are to divide according to their ages, so that each elder son shall receive $24 more than his next younger brother. What is the share of the youngest son?

ELEMENTARY ALGEBRA
Word Problems, Set 3

1. If I take 10 apples from A, he will still have twice as many as B; but if I give them to B, they will each have the same number. How many have they?

2. A gentleman paid for 6 pair of boots and 8 pair of shoes $52; he afterwards paid for 3 pair of boots and 7 pair of shoes $32. How much were the boots and shoes a pair?

3. Says John to William, "I have three times as many marbles as you." "Yes," says William; "but if you will give me 20, I shall have 7 times as many as you." How many has each?

4. A merchant has wines at 9 shillings, and at 13 shillings, per gallon; and he would make a mixture of 100 gallons, that shall be worth 12 shillings per gallon. How many gallons of each must he take?

5. How many gallons of wine, at 9 shillings a gallon, must be mixed with 20 gallons at 13 shillings, that the mixture may be worth 10 shillings a gallon?

6. A man has two silver cups, having but one cover for both. The first cup weighs 12 ounces; and when it is covered, it weighs twice as much as the other cup; but if the second cup be covered, it weighs three times as much as the first. Required the weight of the cover and of the second cup.

7. A builder paid 5 men and 3 boys 42 shillings for working a day; he afterwards hired 7 men and 5 boys a day for 62 shillings. What were the wages of each?

8. Two travellers found some five-dollar bills in the road, of which A secured twice as many as B; but had B secured 5 more of the bills, he would have had 3 times as much money as A. How much did each find?

9. A boy bought 7 oranges and 5 lemons for 55 cents; and afterwards let one of his companions have 4 oranges and 3 lemons for 32 cents, which was their cost. What was the price of each?

10. A man has two horses and two saddles, one of which is worth $40, and the other $5. When the best saddle is upon the first horse, and the worst saddle upon the second, the former is worth just twice as much as the latter; but when the worst saddle is upon the first horse, and the best saddle upon the second, the latter is worth $5 more than the former. What is the value of each horse?

11. A vintner sold to one man 16 dozen of sherry wine and 19 dozen of port, for $382; and to another man, 24 dozen of sherry and 17 dozen of port, for $458; — the prices being the same to both. What was the price of each kind of wine?

12. A man agreed to carry 47 earthen jugs to a certain place. For every one he delivered safe, he was to receive 6 cents; and for every one he broke, he was to pay 10 cents. He received $1.54. How many jugs did he break?

ELEMENTARY ALGEBRA
Word Problems, Set 4

1. Says A to B, "Our ages are the same; but if I were 5 years older, and you were 5 years younger, the product of our ages would be 96." What are their ages?

2. What two numbers are there, whose sum is 25 and product 144?

3. It requires 108 square feet of carpeting to cover a certain entry; and the sum of its length and breadth is equal to twice their difference. How long and wide is it?

4. In a certain orchard there are 4 more rows of trees than there are trees in a row; and if the same number of trees were so arranged that there should be 64 added to each row, the number of the rows would be reduced to 4. How many trees are there in the orchard?

5. A gentleman, being asked the price of his hat, answered, that if it were multiplied by itself, and 26 were subtracted from the product, the remainder multiplied by 5 would be 190. What was the price of the hat?

6. A grass-plot, 18 yards long and 12 wide, is surrounded by a border of flowers of a uniform width. The areas of the grass-plot and border are equal. What is the width of the border?

7. When an army was formed in solid column, there are 9 more men in file than in rank; but when it was formed in 9 lines, each rank was increased by 900 men. Of how many men did the army consist?

ELEMENTARY ALGEBRA
Word Problems, Set 5

1. A man, driving his geese to market, was met by another, who said, "Good morrow, master, with your hundred geese." Said he, "I have not a hundred; but if I had as many more, and half as many more, and two geese and a half, I should have a hundred." How many had he?

2. A laborer agreed to work for a gentleman a year, for $72 and a suit of clothes; but at the end of 7 months, he was dismissed, having received his clothes and $32. What was the value of the clothes?

3. A post, standing in a pond, is $\frac{1}{3}$ of its length under water, and $\frac{1}{4}$ above water, it being 14 feet from the top of the post to the bottom of the pond. What is the whole length of the post?

4. Two friends bought a horse together; and when one had paid $\frac{2}{5}$ and the other $\frac{4}{9}$ of the price agreed upon, they still owed 21 dollars. What was the price of the horse?

5. A merchant retired from business when he had passed $\frac{9}{10}$ of his life, during $\frac{2}{3}$ of which period he had been engaged in trade, having commenced at the age of 21. At what age did he die?

6. Two brothers, A and B, had the same income. A spent all of his, and $\frac{1}{7}$ more; B saved $\frac{1}{5}$ of his. At the end of 10 years, B paid A's debts, and had $160 left. What was their income?

7. A stranger in Boston spent, the first day, $\frac{1}{3}$ of the money he brought with him; the second day, $\frac{1}{4}$; and the third day, $\frac{1}{5}$; when he had only $26 left. How much money did he bring?

8. In an orchard of fruit-trees, $\frac{1}{2}$ of them bear apples, $\frac{1}{4}$ of them pears, $\frac{1}{8}$ of them peaches, 7 trees bear cherries, 3 plums, and 2 quinces. How many trees are there in the orchard?

9. If you divide $50 between two persons, giving one $\frac{3}{7}$ as much as the other, what will be the share of each?

10. A person has a lease for 99 years; and, being asked how much of it had expired, he replied that $\frac{2}{3}$ of the time past was equal to $\frac{4}{5}$ of the time to come. How many years had the lease to run?

11. Two travellers, A and B, began a journey of 300 miles at the same time. A travelled a mile an hour faster than B, and arrived at his journey's end 10 hours before him. How many miles an hour did each travel?

12. A man bought a certain quantity of wine for $94; and after 7 gallons had leaked out, he sold $\frac{1}{4}$ of the remainder, at cost, for $20. How many gallons did he buy?

ELEMENTARY ALGEBRA
Exercises on Fundamental Operations

Find the answers or indicate why they can't be found.

1. $1000 + 60 + 6$

2. $2 + 90 + 400 + 1000$

3. $1.1 + 1.02 + 1.003$

4. $4.23 - 1.1 + 0.011$

5. $3 \cdot 23 \cdot 29$

6. $25 \cdot 25 \cdot 4 \cdot 4$

7. $(0.334)(3) - (0.333)(3)$

8. $\dfrac{1812}{6} - \dfrac{1984}{31}$

9. $3^2 - 2^3$

10. $(1.1)^4 - (1.1)^3$

11. $\dfrac{3}{3} - (5 - 5)$

12. $3 \cdot 2 \cdot 1 \cdot 0$

13. $y - (x - x)$

14. $(7 - 7)(7)$

15. $\dfrac{y - y}{7,777}$

16. $\dfrac{7}{7} \cdot 7$

17. $\dfrac{7}{7 - 7}$

18. $7 - \dfrac{7}{7}$

19. $3x^2 \cdot 0$

20. $3 - (z - z)$

21. $6 + 4 + 6 + 4 + 6 + 4$

22. $6 - 4 + 6 - 4 + 6 - 4$

23. $(6 - 4 + 6) - (4 + 6 - 4)$

24. $3^2 \cdot 5 + 2 \cdot 3^2$

25. $3 \cdot 5^2 + (2 \cdot 3)^2$

26. $1,364 \cdot 7 + 3 \cdot 1,364$

Tell what number should replace ‖‖ in each of the following.

27. $13(‖‖) = 26$

28. $(‖‖)x = 0$

29. $‖‖ - 8 = 2$

30. $x + x + x + x = (‖‖)x$

31. $13y + 28y + 3y = (‖‖)y$

32. $0.121 = (0.11)^{‖‖}$

33. $3^{‖‖} = 3 \cdot 3 \cdot 3 \cdot 3$

Find the values of the following expressions where possible for the numbers given.

$x(x + 1)$

34. if x is 0

35. if x is 1

36. if x is 3

$\dfrac{x + x}{x}$

37. if x is 0

38. if x is 1

39. if x is 3

$x + \dfrac{x}{x}$

40. if x is 0

41. if x is 1

42. if x is 3

$3x^2 + 2x^2 + 5x^2$

43. if x is 0

44. if x is 1

45. if x is 3

$(3 - x)(x)(x - 1)$

46. if x is 1

47. if x is 3

$x^3 - 1$

48. if x is 1

49. if x is 3

$(x - 1)(x^2 + x + 1)$

50. if x is 1

51. if x is 3

ELEMENTARY ALGEBRA
Exercises on the Integers

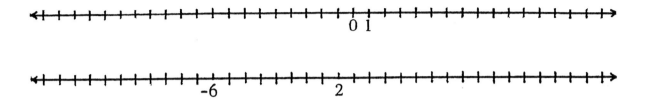

1. Label the following numbers on the first number line above: 10, 2, -18, 7, -10, 12, -5.

2. Label the following numbers on the second number line above: -8, 0, 8, 1, 15, 16, -14.

Circle the smaller number in each of the following pairs. (It may help to think of the numbers in order on a line.)

3. -2, -3

4. 2, -2

5. 0, 11

6. -11, -10

7. $10^3 + 2$, 10^3

8. 10^2, 10^3

9. $(-1)^2$, -1

10. $(-2)^3$, $(-2)^2$

11. -3^2, $(-3)^2$

12. $(-1)^3$, $(-1)^2$

13. $x + 6$, x

14. y, y - 2

15. Plot and label the following points on the graph at the right: A (3, 4), B (1, 6), C (-2, 8), D (-8, 2), E (0, 0), F (5, 5), G (-5, -5), H (-6, 0), I (0, -6), J (-7, -10)

Find the following.

16. 1 + 2 + 3 + 4

17. 1 - 2 + 3 - 4

18. 1 - (2 + 3 - 4)

19. -2 - (1 - 2)

20. 2 - (8 + 1)(-3)

21. (-1)(6 - 5 - 1)(10)

22. $-2 + 3^2$

23. $(-2)^2 + 5 - 1$

24. $(-2)^3 + (-3)^2$

25. $-2^3 + (-3^2)$

26. $\dfrac{12}{-2}$

27. $\dfrac{2 + 4}{2}$

28. $2 + \dfrac{6}{2}$

29. $\dfrac{36}{2 + 2}$

30. $\dfrac{-2}{4 - 6} - 2$

31. $\dfrac{-2 + 4 - 6}{-2}$

32. $(3 - 2)^2 + (2 - 3)^2$

33. $3^2 - 2^2 + 2^2 - 3^2$

34. $3^2 - (2 + 2)^2(-3)^2$

35. $3^2 - (-3)^2$

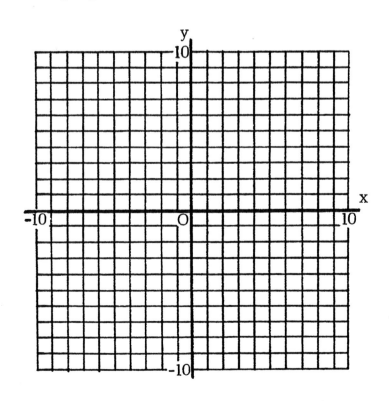

ELEMENTARY ALGEBRA
Exercises on Equations in One Variable:
Area, Perimeter, and Rate

Find ‖‖ so that each of the following is an equivalent pair of equations.

1. $3x + 2 = 11$
   $‖‖x + 20 = 110$

2. $2x + 3 = 9$
   $2x - ‖‖ = 5$

3. $8 - 5x = 17$
   $-5x = ‖‖$

4. $8 + 3x = 14$
   $3x = ‖‖$

5. $2x + 1 = 5 - x$
   $‖‖x - 8 = 0$

6. $2(5 - 4x) = 3 - 5x$
   $‖‖x = 7$

7. $3x - 2(3 - x) = 14$
   $10x - ‖‖ = 0$

8. $x = 6$
   $3(x - 2) = ‖‖$

9. $x^3 + 11 = 38$
   $x^3 = ‖‖$

10. $100 - 2x^2 = 0$
    $2x^2 = ‖‖$

Solve the following equations for x.

11. $3x + 2 = 11$

12. $2x + 3 = 9$

13. $8 - 5x = 17$

14. $8 + 3x = 14$

15. $2x + 1 = 5 - x$

16. $2(5 - 4x) = 3 - 5x$

17. $3x - 2(3 - x) = 14$

Solve for x.

18. $x - 8 = 11$

19. $3x + 8 = 11$

20. $3x + 11 = 13$

21. $x + 2 = 2 - x$

22. $2x + 5 = 3x - 5$

23. $0.5x - 6 = 2.5$

24. $9x = 5(x - 32)$

25. $2(x - 3) + 1 = 5(x + 2)$

26. $x - 0.2(1 - x) = 1$

27. $1 - 3(11 - x) = -13x$

28. $3(x - 1) + 5 = 2(x + 1)$

29. $3x - \dfrac{1}{2} = 2x + \dfrac{9}{2}$

30. $12 + x = 3(x - 1.6)$

Express the perimeters and areas of the following rectangles in terms of x.

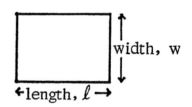

31. The length is twice the width and $w = x$.

32. The length is 1 meter longer than the width and $w = 3x$.

33. The length is 4 meters less than twice the width and $w = x + 2$.

34. Ollie runs a mile in eight minutes. What is his speed in miles per minute?

35. Alice runs at six minutes per mile on the track and half that speed over the obstacle course. How many minutes in all will it take her to run two miles on the track followed by a mile on the obstacle course?

36. What will be her average speed for the three miles covered?

ELEMENTARY ALGEBRA
Exercises on Formulas, Equations, and Problems Having More than One Variable

Solve as indicated. Assume that none of the variables is zero.

1. Solve $y - x = 7$ for x.

2. Solve $PV = 600$ for V.

3. Solve $xyz = 1$ for x.

4. Solve $x(1 + y) = 1 - y$ for x.

5. Solve $x + xy = 1$ for y.

6. Solve $5F - 160 = 9C$ for F.

7. Solve $5F - 160 = 9C$ for C.

8. Solve $4x + 2 = 6 - 2y$ for y.

9. Solve $4x + 2 = 6 - 2y$ for x.

10. Solve $3x + 2y = x$ for x.

11. Solve $\frac{1}{2}at^2 = 16$ for a.

12. Solve $\frac{1}{2}at^2 = 16$ for t^2.

Write the following equations in slope-intercept form and indicate the slope and intercept for each equation.

13. $x + y = 1$

14. $2y - 8x = 6$

15. $x = 2 - y$

16. $3y + 2x - 6 = 0$

17. $6x - y - 11 = -5$

18. $3y - 2x - 1 = x + 5$

19. $x - y + 1 = 0$

20. $x - y + 1 = y - x - 1$

21. From the equations in problems 13-20 find a pair of inconsistent equations and a pair of equivalent equations.

Solve the following pairs of simultaneous equations if possible. Otherwise, indicate whether the equations in the pair are inconsistent or equivalent.

22. $x + y = 3$
$y - x = 25$

23. $3x - 6y = 0$
$5x + 15y = 0$

24. $3x - 6y = 12$
$0x + 2y = 4$

25. $y - x = 0$
$x - y = 1$

26. $3x + y = 6$
$3x - y = 0$

27. $2x + 3y = 29$
$x - 2y = -3$

28. $2x + 3y = 1$
$3x + 4y = 2$

29. $3x + 5y = 1$
$4x + 2y = -8$

30. $3x + 6y = 6$
$x + 2y = 2$

31. $x = y$
$x + y = 3$

32. $4x + 3y = 22$
$2x - 9y = -10$

33. $2x + y = -1$
$8x - 3y = -39$

34. $\frac{1}{2}x - \frac{1}{3}y = 1$
$x - y = 0$

35. $0.5x + y = 2$
$x + y = 1$

36. $2x - 6y = 0$
$3y - x = 0$

37. $4x + 3y = -15$
$2x - 9y = 3$

38. $3x + 2x = 5$
$x + y = 8$

39. $2x + 3y = 4$
$3x + 4y = 5$

40. $1.2x - 0.3y = 0$
$0.2x - 0.2y = 1$

41. $x - 2y = 11$
$4y - 2x = 1$

Graph the pairs of equations in the following problems.

42. Problem 23
43. Problem 25
44. Problem 30
45. Problem 31
46. Problem 36

47. Ollie has 40 coins, some of which are nickels weighing 5 grams each and the rest of which are dimes weighing 2 grams each. If the total weight is 152 grams, what are the coins worth?

48. If the coins weighed 182 grams, what would they be worth?

A stream flows 3 miles per hour. A motorboat takes 5 hours to go upstream from Elmhurst to Forks and 2 hours to go downstream from Forks to Elmhurst.

49. How far is it from Forks to Elmhurst?

50. How fast does the boat go in still water?

ELEMENTARY ALGEBRA
Exercises on Polynomials

Evaluate the following expressions for
$x = -2$, $x = -1$, $x = 0$, $x = 1$, and $x = 2$.

1. $x^2 + 1$

2. $(x - 1)x(x + 1)$

3. $x^3 - x^2 + x + 1$

4. $(x^2 - 1)x(x^2 - 4)$

5. $x^3 + 3x^2 + 6x - 1$

Perform the indicated operations. Write your answers as polynomials in descending powers of the variable.

6. $(3x^3 + 1) + (2x^2 - 5)$

7. $(5x^2 + x - 6) - (2x^2 - 3x + 4)$

8. $(1 + x^2) - (x^3 - 1)$

9. $(3x^3 - 2x^2 + 1) + (2x^2 - x)$

10. $(x^2 + 3x - 1) + (-3x^2 + 5) + (2x - 7)$

11. $(x + 4) + (x^2 - 3) + (x^3 - 2)$

12. $(y^2 + 2y + 1) - (2y + 5)$

13. $(x^2 + x^3) + (2x^3 - 1) - (x + x^3)$

14. $y(1 - y) + (y^2 - 6y + 9)$

15. $(3x^2 + 2x - 1) + 5x + (-5x^2 + 3x - 6)$

16. $(x^5 - 3x^2 + 2) - (x^3 - 2x^2 + x) + (x^4 - 3x)$

17. $(1 - x^2 + x) + (x^3 - 1) - (3 - x^2)$

18. $(5z^3 + 2z^2 - z) - z(z^2 - 1) + 5$

19. $(1 - x)x + (x^2 + 10x + 25) - 16$

20. $(3z - 5)(z + 2)$

21. $(2x - 3)^2$

22. $z(1 - z)^2$

23. $(3 + 2x)(3 - 2x)$

24. $(x^2 + 1)(x - 1)$

25. $(4 + z^2)(2 - z)(2 + z)$

26. $(x + 1)(x - 1)^2$

27. $(3y + 2)(5 - 2y)$

28. $6 + z(z - 1)(z - 2)$

29. $(2 + 5x)(3x - 7)x$

30. $(0.1x - 0.5)(0.2x + 6)$

31. $\dfrac{12x^3 + 6x^2 - 36x}{3x}$

32. $\dfrac{16x^4 - 4x^2}{4x^2 - 1}$

33. $\dfrac{4x^2 - 9}{2x + 3}$

34. $\dfrac{18x^2 - 24x + 8}{3x - 2}$

35. $\dfrac{3x^2 - 2x - 5}{1 + x}$

36. $\dfrac{64x^3 - 27}{4x - 3}$

37. $\dfrac{6x^3 - 16x^2 - 10x + 12}{6x^2 + 2x - 4}$

38. $\dfrac{x^5 + x^3 + 6x^2 - 6x + 18}{x^2 + 3}$

39. $\dfrac{x^6 - 1}{x - 1}$

ELEMENTARY ALGEBRA
Exercises on Factoring

Factor as completely as you can. Write integers in terms of their prime power factors.

1. 550

2. 4,680

3. 1,365

4. 10,000

5. $101^2 - 1$

6. $9^4 - 1$

Factor as completely as you can.

7. $2x^2 - 5x + 2$

8. $16x^2 - 25$

9. $6x^2z - 21xz + 9z$

10. $16z^2 - 4z$

11. $5x^2 + 9x - 2$

12. $4xw^2 + x$

13. $12x^2 + 36x + 27$

14. $x^4 - 16$

15. $a^2x^2 - 6ax + 9$

16. $12x^2 + 17x + 6$

17. $25x^2 - 10x + 1$

18. $25x^2 - 10x$

19. $12x^2 - 17x + 6$

20. $yz^2 + y^2z$

21. $27z^4 - 12z^2$

22. $2xy - 6x + 12y - 36$

23. $2x^5 + 2x^4 - 60x^3$

24. $5w^2x^2 - 3w^2x - 2w^2$

25. $6x^2 - 8x - 168$

26. $27z - 3z^3$

27. $48 - 52y + 12y^2$

28. $15x^2z^2 - 7xz^2 - 30z^2$

29. $w^4 - 8w^2 + 16$

30. $30x^2 - 120$

31. $x^2 + xy - x - y$

32. $6y^4 - 16y^3 - 6y^2$

33. $18xy^2 - 12xy + 8x$

34. $35y^2 + 6y^3 - 6y$

35. $xz + 6z - x - 6$

36. $xy - y^2 - xz + yz$

ELEMENTARY ALGEBRA
Exercises on Fractions

Factor numerators and denominators and reduce to simplest terms. Assume that the denominators are not zero.

1. $\dfrac{18}{81}$

2. $\dfrac{64 \cdot 25 \cdot 36}{99 \cdot 100}$

3. $\dfrac{3ax^2y}{6a^2xy}$

4. $\dfrac{3x^2 - 6y^2}{2y^2 - x^2}$

5. $\dfrac{x^2 - ax}{a^2 - x^2}$

6. $\dfrac{x + 2y}{4y^2 + 4xy + x^2}$

7. $\dfrac{(x^2 - y^2)(x + y)}{(x^2 + y^2)(x - y)}$

8. $\dfrac{7x^2y^2 - 8xy + 1}{28x^2y^2 + 3xy - 1}$

9. $\dfrac{6x^2 - 5x - 6}{(4x^2 - 12x + 9)(9x^2 + 12x + 4)}$

10. $\dfrac{(4x^2 - 9)(25x^2 - 4)}{(10x^2 - 11x - 6)(10x^2 + 11x - 6)}$

Perform the indicated operations. Assume the denominators are not zero. Give your answers in simplest terms.

11. $\dfrac{3}{2} - \dfrac{1}{2}$

12. $\dfrac{1}{2} - \dfrac{1}{3} + \dfrac{1}{6}$

13. $3\dfrac{1}{2} - \dfrac{1}{2}$

14. $\dfrac{1}{3} - 1 + \dfrac{1}{5}$

15. $0.3 + 3 - \dfrac{1}{4}$

16. $0.2 + 1 + \dfrac{2}{3}$

17. $\dfrac{x - 3}{5} - \dfrac{x + 3}{5}$

18. $\dfrac{1}{x} + \dfrac{5}{x^2}$

19. $\dfrac{3}{x} + \dfrac{2}{y} - x$

20. $\dfrac{1}{1 - x} + \dfrac{1}{1 + x}$

21. $\dfrac{x}{y - x} + \dfrac{y}{x - y}$

22. $\dfrac{1 - x}{x} + 1$

23. $\dfrac{x}{1 - x} - 1$

24. $\dfrac{2xy}{x - y} + x - y$

25. $\dfrac{2x}{2x^2 - 7x + 3} - \dfrac{x}{x^2 - 9}$

26. $\dfrac{3}{4} \cdot \dfrac{4}{5} \cdot \dfrac{5}{6} \cdot \dfrac{6}{7}$

27. $\dfrac{30x^2}{y^3} \cdot \dfrac{ay}{6x}$

28. $\dfrac{3a^2x^5y}{12y^3x} \cdot \dfrac{6xy}{5a^4x^3}$

29. $\dfrac{1 - y^2}{35} \cdot \dfrac{5}{y + 1}$

30. $\dfrac{4x}{2x - 10} \cdot \dfrac{x^2 - 5x}{6x}$

(Continued.)

ELEMENTARY ALGEBRA
Exercises on Fractions

31. $\dfrac{x-1}{y^2-1} \cdot \dfrac{y-1}{x^2-1}$

32. $\dfrac{x^2+5x+6}{2x-5} \cdot \dfrac{x}{x^2+6x+9}$

33. $\dfrac{x^2-4}{3x^2-x} \cdot \dfrac{3x^2+2x-1}{x^2+2x}$

34. $\dfrac{y^2-8y+16}{y+1} \cdot \dfrac{y-1}{y^2-y-12}$

35. $\left(1-\dfrac{1}{x}\right)\left(\dfrac{x+1}{x-1}\right)$

36. $\dfrac{3}{2} \div \dfrac{3}{4}$

37. $\dfrac{ax^2y}{x^2+1} \div \dfrac{axy}{27}$

38. $\dfrac{x^3-x}{a^2} \div \dfrac{ax+a}{y}$

39. $\dfrac{2y^2+4y+8}{2y+1} \div \dfrac{y}{4y^2-1}$

40. $\left(\dfrac{x}{y} \div \dfrac{y}{x}\right) \div \dfrac{y}{x}$

41. $\dfrac{x}{y} \div \left(\dfrac{y}{x} \div \dfrac{y}{x}\right)$

Simplify.

42. $\dfrac{\frac{1}{3}-\frac{1}{4}}{\frac{1}{4}-\frac{1}{5}}$

43. $\dfrac{1+\frac{1}{x}}{1-\frac{1}{x}}$

44. $\dfrac{\frac{1}{x}-1}{\frac{1}{x^2}-1}$

45. $\dfrac{x+2}{1-\frac{4}{x^2}}$

46. $\dfrac{1}{1-\frac{1}{1-x}}$

47. $1+\dfrac{1}{1+\frac{2}{x}}$

48. $\dfrac{\frac{x}{x-1}-\frac{x}{x+1}}{\frac{x}{x-1}+\frac{x}{x+1}}$

49. $(1+x^2+x^4)\left(1-\dfrac{1}{x^2}\right)$

50. $\dfrac{2x}{x+y} + \dfrac{2y}{x-y} + \dfrac{x^2+y^2}{y^2-x^2}$

ELEMENTARY ALGEBRA
Exercises on Quadratic Equations

Solve the following equations. You may leave your answers in simple radical form.

1. $(x - 3)(x - 5) = 0$

2. $2x^2 - 8 = 0$

3. $2x^2 - 8x = 0$

4. $9x^2 = 16$

5. $25 - x^2 = 16$

6. $x^2 + 6x + 9 = 0$

7. $x^2 + 6x + 9 = x + 3$

8. $x^2 + 3x - 10 = 0$

9. $x(x - 1) = (x + 1)^2$

10. $2x^2 + 3x = 2$

11. $2x^2 - 3x = 2$

12. $(x - 3)^2 = 25$

13. $x^2 - 15x - 16 = 0$

14. $1 + x - 2x^2 = 0$

15. $6x^2 + 13x + 6 = 0$

16. $x^2 - x - 1 = 0$

17. $x^2 - 3x + 1 = 0$

18. $x^2 - 4x + 3 = 0$

19. $x^2 + 5x + 5 = 0$

20. $x^2 - 2x - 1 = 0$

21. $3x^2 + 4x + 1 = 0$

22. $6x^2 - x - 1 = 0$

23. $x^2 + 3x - 1 = 0$

24. $3x^2 - 5x + 2 = 0$

25. $4x^2 - 8x - 60 = 0$

26. $24x^2 + 42x + 18 = 0$

27. $2x^2 - x = 0$

28. $25x^2 + 0x - 16 = 0$

29. $x^2 - \sqrt{5}x + 1 = 0$

30. $x^2 - 2x + 1 = 0$

31. a) Graph $y = x^2 - 6x$.
    b) Find the discriminant of $x^2 - 6x + 0 = 0$.
    c) How many solutions does the equation in b have?
    d) Solve $x^2 - 6x + 0 = 0$.

32. a) Graph $y = x^2 - 6x + 9$.
    b) Find the discriminant of $x^2 - 6x + 9 = 0$.
    c) How many solutions does the equation in b have?
    d) Solve $x^2 - 6x + 9 = 0$.

33. a) Graph $y = x^2 - 6x + 12$.
    b) Find the discriminant of $x^2 - 6x + 12 = 0$.
    c) How many solutions does the equation in b have?
    d) Solve $x^2 - 6x + 12 = 0$.

Find ▥ so the following expressions are binomial square

34. $x^2 + 6x + ▥$

35. $x^2 + ▥x + 25$

36. $▥x^2 + 4x + 1$

Solve by completing the square. Show your work.

37. $9x^2 + 12x + 3 = 0$

38. $x^2 - 10x + 9 = 0$

39. $25x^2 + 20x + 1 = 0$

40. $x^2 - 18x + 80 = 0$

Factor where possible and solve.

41. $x(x - 1)(x - 2) = 0$

42. $(x + 1)(x^2 + 1) = 0$

43. $(x^2 - 5x + 6)(x + 3) = 0$

44. $6x^3 - 34x^2 + 20x = 0$

45. $x^4 - 16 = 0$

ELEMENTARY ALGEBRA
Exercises on Fractional Equations

Solve the following equations. Check your answers.

1. $\dfrac{x}{3} = \dfrac{5}{6}$

2. $\dfrac{x^2}{4} = x - 1$

3. $\dfrac{x}{x-1} = \dfrac{x-1}{x}$

4. $\dfrac{5x-3}{x+5} = \dfrac{x+1}{x+5}$

5. $\dfrac{x^2+x-3}{x-2} = \dfrac{3}{x-2}$

6. $x + \dfrac{21}{x} = 10$

7. $2x = \dfrac{3-3x}{x+1}$

8. $\dfrac{5}{5-3x} = \dfrac{6x^2-7x}{5-3x}$

9. $\dfrac{6}{x-2} + \dfrac{2}{x-3} = 3$

10. $\dfrac{3}{x-5} + x = 1$

11. $x + 2 = \dfrac{4x+5}{x+2}$

12. $\dfrac{x^2+2x}{x} = x$

13. $\dfrac{x}{x+2} = \dfrac{1}{4-x^2}$

14. $2x - \dfrac{3}{x+3} = \dfrac{x}{x+3}$

15. $\dfrac{x+1}{5} = \dfrac{6}{x}$

16. $x + 1 + \dfrac{x^2-2x-15}{x+3} = 0$

17. $\dfrac{1}{x} + 1 = \dfrac{1}{x+1}$

18. $x + 25 = \dfrac{23x-1}{x-4}$

19. $\dfrac{56}{x} - x = 1$

20. $\dfrac{2}{x^2} - \dfrac{1}{x} - 3 = 0$

21. $\dfrac{3x}{x^2+1} = \dfrac{5x}{x^2+1}$

22. $\dfrac{1}{x} + \dfrac{1}{1+x} = \dfrac{3}{x^2+x}$

23. $\dfrac{1}{3+x} + \dfrac{1}{2+x} = \dfrac{3}{2}$

24. $1 + \dfrac{1}{1+x} = 1 - \dfrac{1}{1-x}$

25. A motorboat travels 5 kilometers per hour in still water.
   a) Find an expression for the time needed for it to go 5 kilometers upstream and return if the current is x kilometers per hour.
   b) Find the current x if it takes the boat 4 hours to go 5 kilometers upstream and return. Give your answer in simple radical form.

ANSWERS

Test 1A

1. $3x$
2. 7^4
3. $y \cdot y$
4. 10^7
5. Not possible.
6. 8^5
7. Yes.
8. $\frac{0}{15} = 0$ because $15 \cdot 0 = 0$.
9. $2x + 10$
10. $5x$
11. $2a + 2b$
12. ab
13. $6x$
14. $2 - y$
15. z^4
16. Figure 3
17. Figure 1
18. Figure 2
19. $x + 2$
20. $y - 20$
21. $(5 \cdot 7)^3$
22. $6(12 - 4)$
23. □
24. □ ○○○
25. □□□□ ○○○○○○ / ○○○○○○
26. □□□□ ○○○○
27. □ ○
28. ○
29. One.
30. $4a + 32$
31. $c^2 - cd$
32. $\frac{y}{1000}$
33. 1000x dollars.
34. 34
35. 63
36. 60
37. 25
38. y
39. $x - y$
40. x nitrogen atoms and 3x hydrogen atoms.
41. $x + 3x$
42. 4
43. $4x$
44. 125
45. 625
46. 3,125
47. Odd.
48. 12
49. 6
50. 2

Extra Credit.
$1 + 2 + 3 + 4 + 5 + 6 + 7 + 8 \cdot 9$

Test 1B

1. $5 - x$
2. y^3
3. $9z$
4. 80
5. 31
6. 24
7. 27
8. □
9. □□□
10. □□□ ○○○○○ / ○○○○○
11. □ ○○○
12. □ ○○○○
13. ○○○○
14. Four.
15. 10^5
16. 11^4
17. Not possible.
18. $4(3 + 15)$
19. $(4 \cdot 6)^2$
20. No.
21. No number times 0 equals 10.
22. $42 + 6a$
23. $cd - d^2$
24. x
25. 0
26. Figure 2.
27. Figure 3.
28. Figure 1.
29. $x - 20$
30. $y + 2$
31. 243
32. 729
33. 2,187
34. Odd.
35. $2x + 8$
36. $4x$
37. $4y$
38. y^2
39. $x + x + x$
40. $2 \cdot 8$
41. 2^5
42. 1000y dollars.
43. $\frac{x}{1000}$
44. 9
45. 4
46. 1
47. x carbon atoms and 2x oxygen atoms.
48. $x + 2x$
49. 3
50. $3x$

Extra Credit.
$1 + 2 + 3 + 4 + 5 + 6 + 7 + 8 \cdot 9$

Test 1C

1. Figure 3.
2. Figure 2.
3. Figure 1.
4. $x + y$
5. x
6. 1000x dollars.
7. $\frac{y}{1000}$
8. $5x$
9. y^2
10. $1 - z$
11. 41
12. 24
13. 100
14. 33
15. $45 + 5a$
16. $xy - y^2$
17. $20 - x$
18. $y - 2$
19. $2a + 4$
20. $2a$
21. $4x$
22. x^2
23. 10^4
24. Not possible.
25. 9^4
26. No.
27. No number times 0 equals 20.
28. $3 \cdot 5$
29. 3^4
30. $x + x$

31. □

32. □○○○○

33. □□□○○○○○○○ (with 888888 pattern)

33. □□□ 888888 / 888888

34. □□□○○○

35. □○

36. ○

37. One.

38. $24 - 2^3$

39. $3(7 + 5)$

40. 216

41. 1,296

42. 7,776

43. Even.

44. 16

45. 9

46. 4

47. x carbon atoms and 4x hydrogen atoms.

48. x + 4x

49. 5

50. 5x

Extra Credit.

$1 + 2 + 3 + 4 + 5 + 6 + 7 + 8 \cdot 9$

Test 1D

1. $2(1 + 8)$

2. $40 - 6^2$

3. $x - 2$

4. $20 - y$

5. 8^5

6. $3y$

7. $x \cdot x \cdot x \cdot x \cdot x \cdot x$

8. $3a + 21$

9. $x^2 - xy$

10. 0

11. y

12. $\dfrac{x}{1000}$

13. 1000y dollars.

14. □

15. □□

16. □□ 88888 / 88888

17. □○○○○○

18. □○○○○○○

19. ○○○○○

20. Six.

21. $\dfrac{2}{x}$

22. $9 - y$

23. z^3

24. $2a + 12$

25. $6a$

26. $2x + 2y$

27. xy

28. 9

29. 147

30. 53

31. 30

32. Figure 2.

33. Figure 1.

34. Figure 3.

35. 10^8

36. 12^4

37. Not possible.

38. Yes.

39. $\dfrac{0}{25} = 0$ because $25 \cdot 0 = 0$.

40. 20

41. 12

42. 6

43. 2x nitrogen atoms and x oxygen atoms.

44. $2x + x$

45. 3

46. $3x$

47. 256

48. 1,024

49. 4,096

50. Even.

Extra Credit.

$1 + 2 + 3 + 4 + 5 + 6 + 7 + 8 \cdot 9$

Test 2A

1.
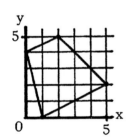

2.

x	1	2	3	4	5
y	2	5	8	11	14

3.

x	0	1	2	3	4
y	0	3	8	15	24

4.

x	5	6	7	8	9
y	0	6	14	24	36

5. True.

6. True.

7. False.

8. True.

9. $y = x^2$

10. $y = 9 - x$

11. $y = \dfrac{x}{2}$

12. $y = 5x + 2$

13.

x	1	2	3	4
y	5	6	7	8

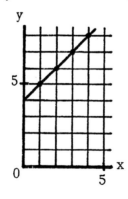

14.

x	1	2	3	4
y	8	6	4	2

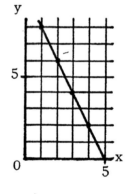

2   Answers

15.

x	1	2	3	4
y	6	3	2	$1\frac{1}{2}$

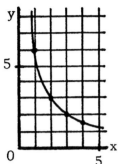

16. $y = \dfrac{150}{x}$

17. 150

18. Inversely.

19. A curved line.

20.

x	20	30	40	50	60
y	16	24	32	40	48

21. A direct variation (or, a linear function).

22. A straight line through the origin.

Extra Credit.

1. $y = 3x^2$

2. $y = 16 - 3x$

Test 2B

1.

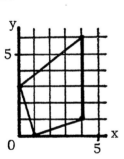

2.

x	2	3	4	5	6
y	1	3	5	7	9

3.

x	0	1	2	3	4
y	2	3	10	29	66

4.

x	0	1	2	3	4
y	0	5	12	21	32

5. True.

6. True.

7. True.

8. False.

9. $y = \dfrac{x}{3}$

10. $y = x^2$

11. $y = 7 - x$

12. $y = 4x + 1$

13.

x	1	2	3	4
y	4	5	6	7

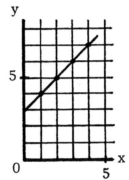

14.

x	1	2	3	4
y	4	2	$1\frac{1}{3}$	1

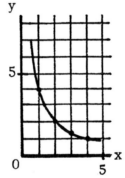

15.

x	1	2	3	4
y	6	4	2	0

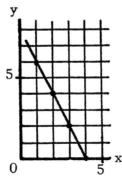

16. $y = \dfrac{240}{x}$

17. 240

18. Inversely.

19. A curved line.

20.

x	20	30	40	50	60
y	14	21	28	35	42

21. A direct variation (or, a linear function).

22. A straight line through the origin.

Extra Credit.

1. $y = 5x^2$

2. $y = 14 - 3x$

Test 2C

1.

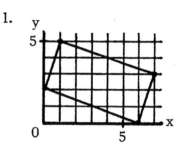

2.

x	1	2	3	4	5
y	3	7	11	15	19

3.

x	0	1	2	3	4
y	0	4	10	18	28

4.

x	2	3	4	5	6
y	0	3	8	15	24

5. False.

6. False.

7. True.

8. True.

9. $y = 2x + 5$

10. $y = \dfrac{x}{4}$

11. $y = x^3$

12. $y = 6 - x$

13.

x	1	2	3	4
y	6	7	8	9

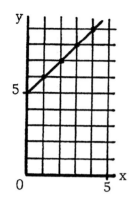

14.

x	1	2	3	4
y	7	5	3	1

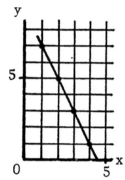

15.

x	1	2	3	4
y	8	4	$2\frac{2}{3}$	2

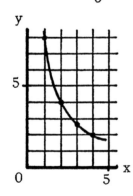

16.

x	20	30	40	50	60
y	12	18	24	30	36

17. A direct variation (or, a linear function).

18. A straight line through the origin.

19. $y = \dfrac{300}{x}$

4   Answers

20. 300

21. Inversely.

22. A curved line.

Extra Credit.

1. $y = 2x^3$

2. $y = 15 - 2x$

Test 2D

1.

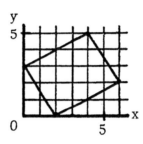

2.

x	1	2	3	4	5
y	1	4	7	10	13

3.

x	0	1	2	3	4
y	1	2	9	28	65

4.

x	0	1	2	3	4
y	0	6	14	24	36

5. False.

6. False.

7. False.

8. True.

9. $y = 10 - x$

10. $y = x^3$

11. $y = 6x + 1$

12. $y = \dfrac{x}{5}$

13.

x	1	2	3	4
y	3	4	5	6

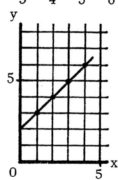

14.

x	1	2	3	4
y	6	3	2	$1\frac{1}{2}$

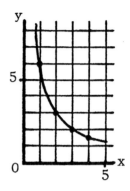

15.

x	1	2	3	4
y	9	6	3	0

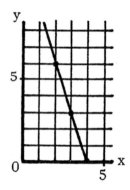

16.

x	20	30	40	50	60
y	18	27	36	45	54

17. A direct variation (or, a linear function).

18. A straight line through the origin.

19. $y = \dfrac{180}{x}$

20. 180

21. Inversely.

22. A curved line.

Extra Credit.

1. $y = 6x^2$

2. $y = 13 - 2x$

Test 3A

1. True.
2. False.
3. True.
4. True.
5. 24
6. 96
7. -9
8. -10
9. $x > -2$
10. $x^2 < \frac{1}{2}x$
11. $x - 3 = 5$
12.
1	-7
-4	-12
-8	-24
-2	-18
-1	-9
-2	-2
13. □
    □•••••
    □□•••••
    □□•••••
    □□•••
    □••
    ••
14. -2
15. -15
16. -20
17. 8
18. 11
19. >
20. <
21. =
22. >
23. 2
24. 11
25. -5
26. 7
27. 9
28. -x

29. $-\frac{x}{y}$
30. 14
31. -18
32. -48
33. -64
34. -480
35. $y = -2x$

x	0	1	2	3
y	0	-2	-4	-6

   $y = x + 3$

x	0	1	2	3
y	3	4	5	6

36.

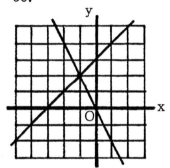

37. (-1, 2)
38. 35
39. -17
40. 77
41. 96 feet per second.
42. 0 feet per second.
43. -32 feet per second.
44. The ball is at the top of its path.
45. The ball is moving down.

Extra Credit.
   1. 14,400
   2. $\frac{4x}{5}$

Test 3B

1. True.
2. True.
3. False.
4. False.
5. -12
6. -6
7. 15
8. 40
9. $x < -2$
10. $\frac{1}{2}x > x^2$
11. $\frac{x}{3} = 5$
12.
1	-7
-2	-10
-8	-40
0	-32
0	-8
-1	-1
13. □
    □•••
    □□□□•••••
    □□□□••••
    □•
    •
14. 8
15. 3
16. 3
17. -7
18. -27
19. >
20. =
21. >
22. <
23. 3
24. 13
25. -4
26. 5
27. 6

28. -1
29. -y
30. -360
31. 7
32. 27
33. -18
34. -36
35. $y = x + 4$

x	0	1	2	3
y	4	5	6	7

   $y = -3x$

x	0	1	2	3
y	0	-3	-6	-9

36.

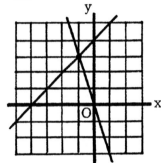

37. (-1, 3)
38. 9
39. 33
40. -26
41. 64 feet per second.
42. 0 feet per second.
43. -32 feet per second.
44. The ball is at the top of its path.
45. The ball is moving down.

Extra Credit.
   1. 11,200
   2. $\frac{4x}{5}$

Test 3C

1. False.
2. True.
3. False.
4. True.
5. 108
6. -20
7. -4
8. 22
9. x > 2
10. $x^3 < 2x$
11. x - 4 = -1
12.

1	-7
2	-14
-8	-24
-4	-12
-3	-11
-4	-4

13. □
□□
□□●●●●●
□●●●●●
□●●●●
●●●●
14. -11
15. 4
16. 9
17. -16
18. 5
19. =
20. >
21. >
22. <
23. 12
24. 2
25. 4
26. -7
27. 7
28. 0
29. -1

30. -49
31. 19
32. -420
33. 2
34. -100
35. y = x + 6

x	0	1	2	3
y	6	7	8	9

y = -2x

x	0	1	2	3
y	0	-2	-4	-6

36.
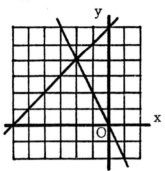

37. (-2, 4)
38. 4
39. -28
40. 11
41. 32 feet per second.
42. 0 feet per second.
43. -64 feet per second.
44. The ball is at the top of its path.
45. The ball is moving down.

Extra Credit.

1. 9,600

2. $\dfrac{4x}{5}$

Test 3D

1. False.
2. False.
3. True.
4. False.
5. -3
6. 28
7. 36
8. -18
9. x < 2
10. $2x > x^3$
11. $\dfrac{x}{4} = -1$
12.

1	-7
3	-21
-9	-33
-3	-11
-2	-10
-3	-3

13. □
□□□
□□□●●●●●●
□●●●●
□●●●
●●●
14. 7
15. -36
16. -13
17. 5
18. 4
19. =
20. >
21. <
22. >
23. 10
24. 1
25. 4
26. -7
27. 8
28. x

29. $-\dfrac{y}{x}$
30. -240
31. 8
32. -14
33. 25
34. -81
35. y = -x

x	0	1	2	3
y	0	-1	-2	-3

y = x - 4

x	0	1	2	3
y	-4	-3	-2	-1

36.
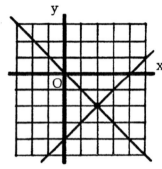

37. (2, -2)
38. 30
39. 55
40. -23
41. 128 feet per second.
42. 0 feet per second.
43. -32 feet per second.
44. The ball is at the top of its path.
45. The ball is moving down.

Extra Credit.

1. 12,800

2. $\dfrac{4x}{5}$

Test 4A

1. $\dfrac{-4}{1}$

2. $\dfrac{7}{10}$

3. $\dfrac{16}{5}$

4. 2.25

5. -1.3

6. 0.125

7. =

8. <

9. >

10. >

11. =

12. <

13. -11

14. 3.6

15. -5.8

16. -1.4

17. -2.2

18. -0.72

19. -1.4

20. -0.5

21. 0.0625

22. -8

23. -0.1

24. 8.5

25. 4.1

26. 0

27. -3

28.
2.1	-0.6	-7.3
7.1	4.4	-2.3
14.2	8.8	-4.6
7.2	1.8	-11.6
3.6	0.9	-5.8
1.5	1.5	1.5

29. 1.5

30. 7

31. -5.2

32. 2.07

33. -13

34. 0.04

35. 0.37

36. 1.19

37. 0.00

38.
x	-3	-2	-1	0
y	4	-1	-4	-5

x	1	2	3
y	-4	-1	4

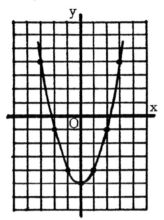

39.
x	0	1	2	3	4
y	7	4	1	-2	-5

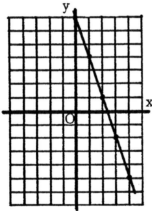

40.
x	-4	-3	-2	-1	0
y	1	$1\frac{1}{3}$	2	4	—

x	1	2	3	4
y	-4	-2	$-1\frac{1}{3}$	-1

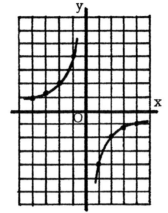

41.
x	-3	-2	-1	0
y	$-7\frac{1}{2}$	-5	$-2\frac{1}{2}$	0

x	1	2	3
y	$2\frac{1}{2}$	5	$7\frac{1}{2}$

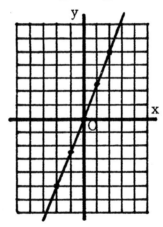

42. $y = -3x + 7$ and $y = 2.5x$ (39 and 41)

43. $y = 2.5x$ (41)

44. $y = x^2 - 5$ and $y = \dfrac{-4}{x}$ (38 and 40)

45. $y = \dfrac{-4}{x}$ (40)

Extra Credit.

5

Test 4B

1. $\dfrac{0}{1}$

2. $\dfrac{-23}{10}$

3. $\dfrac{25}{4}$

4. -7.4

5. 0.25

6. 0.096

7. <

8. =

9. <

10. >

11. >

12. =

13. -3.6

14. -4.8

15. -2.52

16. 7

17. -11

18. 5.4

19. -6.6

20. -3.3

21. -0.62

22. 0.0961

23. -10

24. -1.8

25. 0

26. -2

27. 7.4

28.
4.5	-0.2	-3.1
0.5	-4.2	-7.1
1.5	-12.6	-21.3
7.5	-6.6	-15.3
2.5	-2.2	-5.1
-2	-2	-2

29. -2

30. 6

31. -4.3

32. 1.85

33. -1

34. 0.03

35. 0.27

36. 3.19

37. 0.00

38.

x	-3	-2	-1	0
y	$4\frac{1}{2}$	3	$1\frac{1}{2}$	0

x	1	2	3
y	$-1\frac{1}{2}$	-3	$-4\frac{1}{2}$

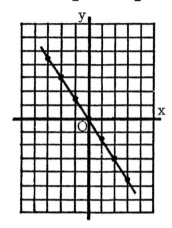

39.

x	-3	-2	-1	0
y	11	6	3	2

x	1	2	3
y	3	6	11

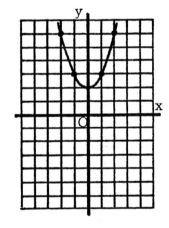

40.

x	0	1	2	3
y	-7	-5	-3	-1

x	4	5
y	1	3

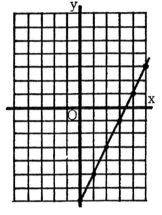

41.

x	-4	-3	-2	-1	0
y	$1\frac{1}{4}$	$1\frac{2}{3}$	$2\frac{1}{2}$	5	—

x	1	2	3	4
y	-5	$-2\frac{1}{2}$	$-1\frac{2}{3}$	$-1\frac{1}{4}$

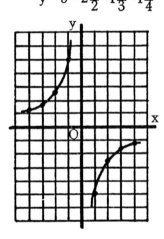

42. $y = -1.5x$ and $y = 2x - 7$ (38 and 40)

43. $y = -1.5x$ (38)

44. $y = x^2 + 2$ and $y = \dfrac{-5}{x}$ (39 and 41)

45. $y = \dfrac{-5}{x}$ (41)

Extra Credit.

8

Test 4C

1. $\dfrac{-1}{1}$

2. $\dfrac{67}{100}$

3. $\dfrac{9}{2}$

4. -3.5

5. 0.09

6. 0.625

7. >

8. =

9. >

10. <

11. >

12. =

13. -0.28

14. 0.0196

15. -12.2

16. 3

17. -4.7

18. -2.5

19. -1.6

20. -3.2

21. -1.92

22. -3

23. 6.2

24. -10

25. -4

26. 3.2

27. 0

28.

3.7	0.4	-1.6
7.4	0.8	-3.2
0.4	-6.2	-10.2
0.2	-3.1	-5.1
4.2	0.9	-1.1
0.5	0.5	0.5

29. 0.5

30. 9

31. -2.5

32. 3.16

33. -9

34. 0.05

35. 0.53

36. 0.00

37. 1.09

38.

x	-4	-3	-2	-1	0
y	$-1\frac{1}{2}$	-2	-3	-6	—

x	1	2	3	4
y	6	3	2	$1\frac{1}{2}$

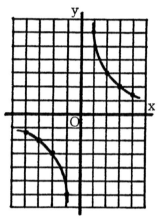

39.

x	-3	-2	-1	0
y	$-4\frac{1}{2}$	-3	$-1\frac{1}{2}$	0

x	1	2	3
y	$1\frac{1}{2}$	3	$4\frac{1}{2}$

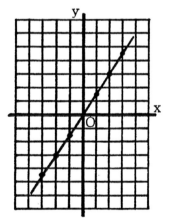

40.

x	-3	-2	-1	0
y	-5	0	3	4

x	1	2	3
y	3	0	-5

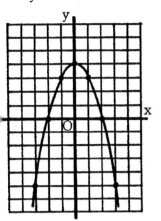

41.

x	0	1	2	3
y	5	3	1	-1

x	4	5
y	-3	-5

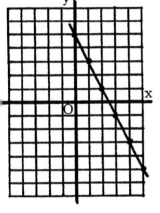

42. $y = 1.5x$ and
$y = -2x + 5$ (39 and 41)

43. $y = 1.5x$ (39)

44. $y = \frac{6}{x}$ and

$y = 4 - x^2$ (38 and 40)

45. $y = \frac{6}{x}$ (38)

Extra Credit.

1

Test 4D

1. $\frac{5}{1}$

2. $\frac{-8}{100}$

3. $\frac{7}{3}$

4. 0.7

5. 6.25

6. -0.375

7. <

8. >

9. =

10. =

11. <

12. >

13. -3.1

14. -8.6

15. -3.3

16. -3.9

17. -1.08

18. 12

19. -7.4

20. 4

21. 0.0324

22. -0.36

23. -2.6

24. 0

25. 5.1

26. -2

27. -10

28.

7.2	0.6	-1.8
3.6	0.3	-0.9
0.6	-2.7	-3.9
1.2	-5.4	-7.8
6.2	-0.4	-2.8
-1	-1	-1

29. -1

30. 8

31. -3.2

32. 4.57

33. -7

34. 0.01

35. 0.13

36. 0.00

37. 1.44

38.

x	0	1	2	3	4
y	-4	-1	2	5	8

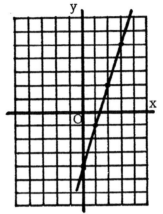

39.

x	-3	-2	-1	0
y	$7\frac{1}{2}$	5	$2\frac{1}{2}$	0

x	1	2	3
y	$-2\frac{1}{2}$	-5	$-7\frac{1}{2}$

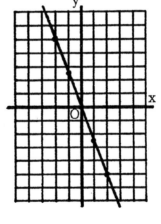

40.

x	-4	-3	-2	-1
y	$-1\frac{1}{4}$	$-1\frac{2}{3}$	$-2\frac{1}{2}$	-5

x	0	1	2	3	4
y	—	5	$2\frac{1}{2}$	$1\frac{2}{3}$	$1\frac{1}{4}$

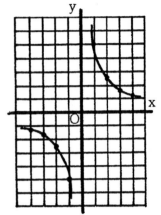

41.

x	-3	-2	-1	0
y	-2	3	6	7

x	1	2	3
y	6	3	-2

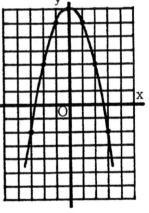

42. $y = 3x - 4$ and
$y = -2.5x$ (38 and 39)

43. $y = -2.5x$ (39)

44. $y = \frac{5}{x}$ and

$y = 7 - x^2$ (40 and 41)

45. $y = \frac{5}{x}$ (40)

Extra Credit.

4

Test 5A

1. True.
2. Neither.
3. -2
4. 10
5. 0
6. 2 and -3
7. 0 and -4
8. Add 2 and divide by 5.
9. Multiply by 4 and subtract 9.
10. -12.5
11. -4
12. -25
13. $x^2 - 5x$
14. $(x - 5)x$
15. $9 + x$
16. $4x$
17. $18x$
18. $8x$
19. $4x^2$
20. -7
21. 60
22. -8
23. 0.5
24. 0
25. 11, 13, and 15
26. 8 and 9
27. 24
28. 7
29. 31
30. Citation, 48x feet; Whirlaway, 54x feet.
31. Citation

Citation: 51, 48x; Whirlaway: 54x

32. $51 + 48x = 54x$
33. 8.5
34. Citation, 408 feet; Whirlaway, 459 feet.

Extra Credit.

34 years old.

Test 5B

1. False.
2. True.
3. 15
4. -3
5. No number, because no number equals itself increased by 4.
6. 4 and -2
7. 0 and -5
8. Add 5 and divide by 2.
9. Multiply by 9 and subtract 4.
10. -13.5
11. -8
12. -18
13. $(x - 6)x$
14. $x^2 - 6x$
15. $3x$
16. $20x$
17. $8 + x$
18. $6x^2$
19. $12x$
20. -5
21. -11
22. 64
23. 0
24. 0.25
25. 10, 12, and 16
26. 7 and 9
27. 6
28. 22
29. 28
30. Citation, 47x feet; Whirlaway, 55x feet.
31. Citation

Citation: 52, 47x; Whirlaway: 55x

32. $52 + 47x = 55x$
33. 6.5
34. Citation, 305.5 feet; Whirlaway, 357.5 feet.

Extra Credit.

29 years old.

Test 5C

1. Neither.
2. False.
3. -7
4. No number, because no number equals itself decreased by 10.
5. -2
6. 3 and -2
7. 0 and -8
8. Subtract 2 and divide by 3.
9. Multiply by 5 and add 7.
10. -10.5
11. -2
12. -24.5
13. $x^2 + 8x$
14. $(x + 8)x$
15. $10x$
16. $5x^2$
17. $11 + x$
18. $5x$
19. $8x$
20. -4
21. 48
22. -12
23. 0
24. -0.5
25. 8, 11, and 17
26. 4 and 6
27. 46
28. 10
29. 36
30. Citation, 45x feet; Whirlaway, 51x feet.
31. Citation

Citation: 57, 45x; Whirlaway: 51x

32. $57 + 45x = 51x$
33. 9.5
34. Citation, 427.5 feet; Whirlaway, 484.5 feet.

Extra Credit.

31 years old.

Test 5D

1. Neither.
2. True.
3. -6
4. 128
5. -4
6. 4 and -1
7. 0 and 6
8. Subtract 3 and divide by 2.
9. Multiply by 7 and add 5.
10. -10.8
11. -5
12. -16.2
13. $(x + 3)x$

14. $x^2 + 3x$

15. $14x$

16. $3x^2$

17. $6x$

18. $13 + x$

19. $7x$

20. -8

21. -6

22. 0

23. 105

24. 0.2

25. $7, 12,$ and 15

26. 3 and 11

27. 38

28. 30

29. 8

30. Citation, $42x$ feet; Whirlaway, $50x$ feet.

31.

Citation

|—44—|—42x—|

|———50x———|

Whirlaway

32. $44 + 42x = 50x$

33. 5.5

34. Citation, 231 feet; Whirlaway, 275 feet.

Extra Credit.

27 years old.

Test 6A

1. -2

2. -46

3. Yes.

4. Yes.

5. $(9, 1)$ and $(4, 2)$

6. $(1, 121), (11, 11),$ and $(121, 1)$

7. $x = \dfrac{y + 5}{3}$

8. $y = \dfrac{6 - x}{4}$

9. $e = ir$

10. $r = \dfrac{e}{i}$

11. $h = 24 - 5t$

12. 9 centimeters

13. $x - 3y = 9$; $a = 1, \ b = -3, \ c = 9$

14. $2x = 20$; $a = 2, \ b = 0, \ c = 20$

15. x-intercept, 4; y-intercept, -18

16. x-intercept, 10; y-intercept, 16

17. $\dfrac{2}{5}$

18. -4

19.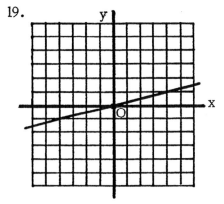

20.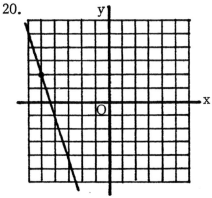

21. Slope, 7; y-intercept, -3

22. Slope, 0; y-intercept, $\dfrac{1}{2}$

23.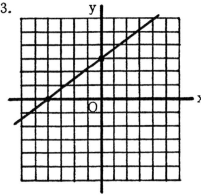

24.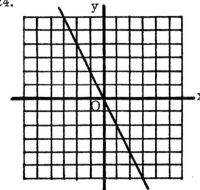

25.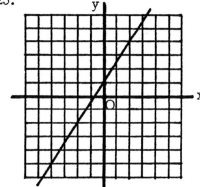

Extra Credit.

$(19, 3)$

Test 6B

1. -1

2. -61

3. No.

4. Yes.

5. $(1, 49), (7, 7),$ and $(49, 1)$

6. $(9, 1)$ and $(3, 2)$

7. $x = \dfrac{y - 5}{2}$

8. $y = \dfrac{4 - x}{6}$

9. $k = pv$

10. $v = \dfrac{k}{p}$

11. $h = 21 - 4t$

12. 13 centimeters

13. $x + 2y = 8$;
    $a = 1$, $b = 2$, $c = 8$

14. $3y = 13$;
    $a = 0$, $b = 3$, $c = 13$

15. x-intercept, 8;
    y-intercept, 10

16. x-intercept, 15;
    y-intercept, -35

17. $\dfrac{3}{5}$

18. -2

19.
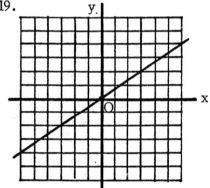

20.
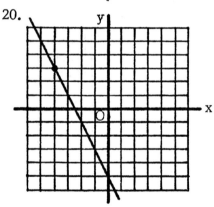

21. Slope, 3; y-intercept, -7

22. Slope, -1; y-intercept, 0

23.
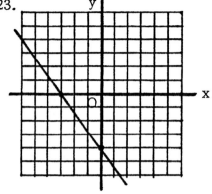

24.
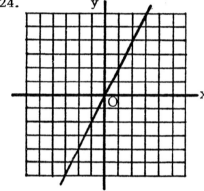

25.
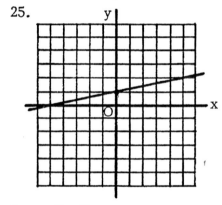

Extra Credit.

    (13, 3)

Test 6C

1. -8

2. -78

3. Yes.

4. No.

5. (12, 1) and (3, 2)

6. (1, 25), (5, 5), and (25, 1)

7. $x = \dfrac{y + 3}{5}$

8. $y = \dfrac{8 - x}{2}$

9. $w = fs$

10. $s = \dfrac{w}{f}$

11. $h = 20 - 3t$

12. 8 centimeters

13. $4x + y = 6$;
    $a = 4$, $b = 1$, $c = 6$

14. $5x = 2$;
    $a = 5$, $b = 0$, $c = 2$

15. x-intercept, 14;
    y-intercept, 4

16. x-intercept, 18;
    y-intercept, -12

17. $\dfrac{4}{5}$

18. -3

19.
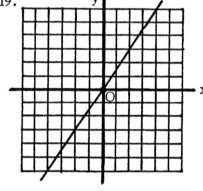

20.
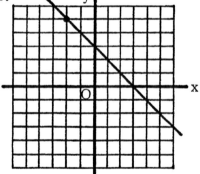

21. Slope, 2; y-intercept, -9

22. Slope, 0; y-intercept, $\dfrac{1}{5}$

23.

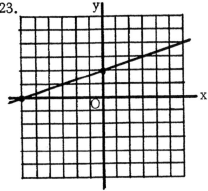

24.

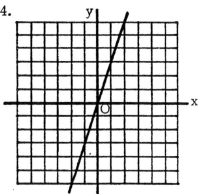

25.

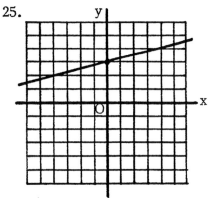

Extra Credit.

   (11, 3)

Test 6D

1. -9

2. -31

3. No.

4. Yes.

5. (1, 9), (3, 3) and (9, 1)

6. (12, 1) and (4, 2)

7. $x = \dfrac{y - 1}{4}$

8. $y = \dfrac{7 - x}{5}$

9. $i = rp$

10. $p = \dfrac{i}{r}$

11. $h = 17 - 2t$

12. 5 centimeters

13. $2x + y = 10$;
   $a = 2$, $b = 1$, $c = 10$

14. $4y = 5$;
   $a = 0$, $b = 4$, $c = 5$

15. x-intercept, 10;
   y-intercept, -6

16. x-intercept, 36;
   y-intercept, 8

17. $\dfrac{1}{6}$

18. -5

19.

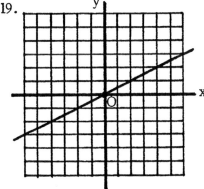

20.

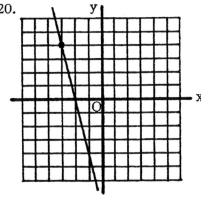

21. Slope, 9; y-intercept, -2

22. Slope, 1; y-intercept, 0

23.

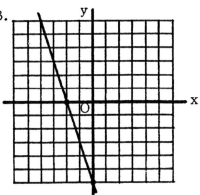

24.

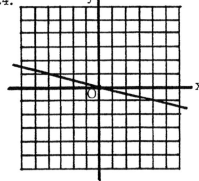

25.

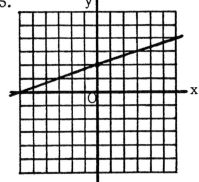

Extra Credit.

   (17, 3)

Test 7A

1. Yes.

2. No.

3. $9x = 33$

4. $x + 12y = 9$

5. $2x - 3y = 6$

6. (To be solved by addition
   or subtraction.)
   (9.5, 14)

7. (To be solved by addition
   or subtraction.)
   (-6, 7)

8. (To be solved by addition or subtraction.)
(8, -3)

9.
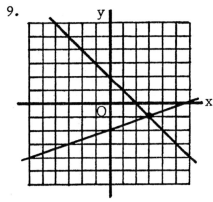

The equations have one solution: (3, -1).

10.
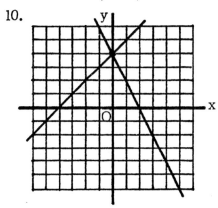

The equations have one solution: (0, 4).

11.
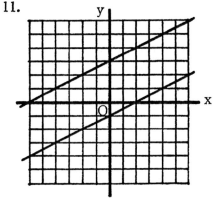

The equations have no solutions.

12. (To be solved by substitution.)
(7, 35)

13. (To be solved by substitution.)
(-1, 2)

14. (To be solved by substitution.)
(3, 19)

15. $x + y = 14$, $9x = 12y$

16. (8, 6)

17. $x + y = 220$,
$7x + 12y = 1,840$

18. (160, 60)

19. 160 packages weighing 7 pounds each and 60 packages weighing 12 pounds each.

Extra Credit.

(8, -3, 15)

Test 7B

1. No.

2. Yes.

3. $18x = 36$

4. $2x + 4y = 8$

5. $4x - y = 7$

6. (To be solved by addition or subtraction.)
(4.5, 13)

7. (To be solved by addition or subtraction.)
(-8, 5)

8. (To be solved by addition or subtraction.)
(9, -2)

9.
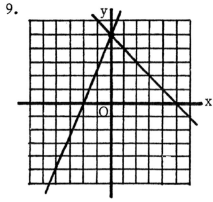

The equations have one solution: (0, 5).

10.
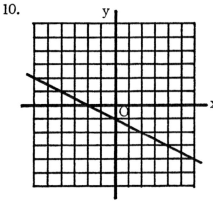

The equations have infinitely many solutions.

11.
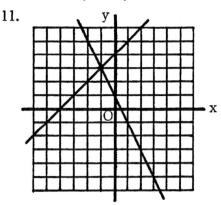

The equations have one solution: (-1, 3).

12. (To be solved by substitution.)
(18, 9)

13. (To be solved by substitution.)
(5, -1)

14. (To be solved by substitution.)
(15, 2)

15. $x + y = 15$, $15x = 10y$

16. (6, 9)

17. $x + y = 180$,
$6x + 13y = 1,570$

18. (110, 70)

19. 110 packages weighing 6 pounds each and 70 packages weighing 13 pounds each.

Extra Credit.

(9, -2, 13)

Test 7C

1. Yes.
2. Yes.
3. $13x = 32$
4. $x + 20y = 16$
5. $3x - 5y = 4$
6. (To be solved by addition or subtraction.)
   (16, 7.5)
7. (To be solved by addition or subtraction.)
   (9, -5)
8. (To be solved by addition or subtraction.)
   (-2, 8)
9.

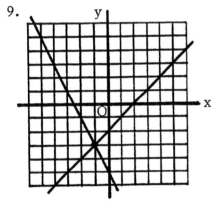

The equations have one solution: (-1, -3).

10.

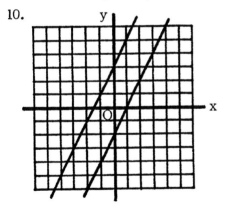

The equations have no solutions.

11.

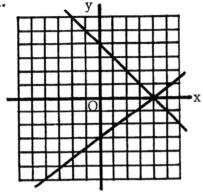

The equations have one solution: (4, 0).

12. (To be solved by substitution.)
    (8, 32)
13. (To be solved by substitution.)
    (-2, 3)
14. (To be solved by substitution.)
    (2, 17)
15. $x + y = 32$, $3x = 5y$
16. (20, 12)
17. $x + y = 190$,
    $8x + 15y = 1,870$
18. (140, 50)
19. 140 packages weighing 8 pounds each and 50 packages weighing 15 pounds each.

Extra Credit.

(7, -4, 12)

Test 7D

1. No.
2. No.
3. $9x = 50$
4. $5x + 16y = 14$
5. $x - 4y = 9$
6. (To be solved by addition or subtraction.)
   (18, 3.5)
7. (To be solved by addition or subtraction.)
   (7, -3)
8. (To be solved by addition or subtraction.)
   (-4, 9)
9.

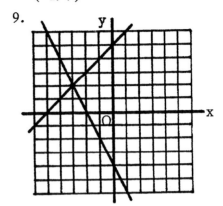

The equations have one solution: (-3, 2).

10.

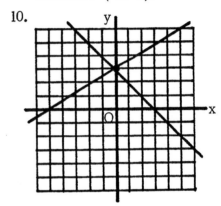

The equations have one solution: (0, 3).

11.

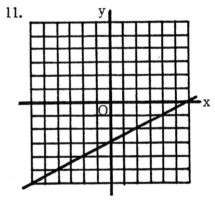

The equations have infinitely many solutions.

12. (To be solved by substitution.)
    (24, 8)
13. (To be solved by substitution.)
    (3, -1)

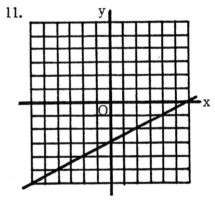

Answers   15

14. (To be solved by substitution.)
    (19, 3)
15. $x + y = 30,$
    $6x = 4y$
16. (12, 18)
17. $x + y = 210$
    $5x + 14y = 1,770$
18. (130, 80)
19. 130 packages weighing 5 pounds each and 80 packages weighing 14 pounds each.

Extra Credit.

   (6, -5, 14)

Test 8A

1. 10^{10}
2. 9×10^8
3. 10^{-6}
4. 25,000
5. 0.0000801
6. 4×10^3
7. 3.9×10^7
8. 1.7×10^{-4}
9. 5×10^{-13}
10. -243
11. 1
12. $\frac{1}{16}$
13. $-\frac{1}{6}$
14. x^{-5}
15. x^{-24}
16. x^7
17. x^{-5}
18. <
19. <
20. =
21. >
22. $64x^6$

23. $-y^{21}$
24. $\frac{x^8}{y^4}$
25. 4.2×10^{14}
26. 1.5×10^6
27. 5×10^2
28. 3.43×10^{14}
29. <
30. >
31. =
32. >
33. 9
34. 14
35. 3
36. 10
37. 3.7×10^9 and 4.9×10^8
38. Approximately 7.6.
39.

x	0	1	2	3
y	1.5	3	6	12

40.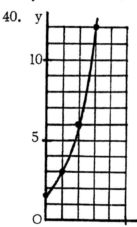

Extra Credit.

One million inches is approximately 16 miles; so it would take several hours.

Test 8B

1. 10^8
2. 9×10^7

3. 10^{-5}
4. 250,000
5. 0.00801
6. 4×10^2
7. 3.9×10^5
8. 1.7×10^{-5}
9. 5×10^{-12}
10. 1
11. $\frac{1}{125}$
12. -128
13. $-\frac{1}{8}$
14. x^{-1}
15. x^{-30}
16. x^{11}
17. x^{-3}
18. >
19. >
20. <
21. =
22. $256x^4$
23. $-y^{15}$
24. $\frac{x^6}{y^{12}}$
25. 5.6×10^{16}
26. 2×10^6
27. 6×10^3
28. 2.16×10^{14}
29. >
30. <
31. >
32. =
33. 10
34. 16
35. 8
36. 3
37. 2.8×10^9 and 6.7×10^7
38. Approximately 42.

39.

x	0	1	2	3
y	4	2	1	0.5

40.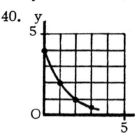

Extra Credit.

One million inches is approximately 16 miles; so it would take several hours.

Test 8C

1. 10^{11}
2. 9×10^6
3. 10^{-8}
4. 2,500,000
5. 0.0801
6. 2×10^4
7. 3.9×10^9
8. 1.7×10^{-2}
9. 5×10^{-15}
10. -64
11. $\frac{1}{32}$
12. 1
13. $-\frac{1}{3}$
14. x^{-3}
15. x^{-28}
16. x^{10}
17. x^{-7}
18. <
19. >
20. >
21. =
22. $125x^3$
23. $-y^{10}$

24. $\dfrac{x^{24}}{y^6}$

25. 6.3×10^{17}

26. 2×10^5

27. 5×10^4

28. 1.25×10^{14}

29. $=$

30. $>$

31. $>$

32. $<$

33. 18

34. 11

35. 5

36. 12

37. 1.8×10^9 and 1.4×10^8

38. Approximately 13.

39.

x	0	1	2	3
y	0.5	1	2	4

40.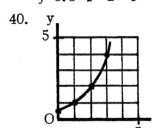

Extra Credit.

One million inches is approximately 16 miles; so it would take several hours.

Test 8D

1. 10^7
2. 9×10^9
3. 10^{-7}
4. 2,500
5. 0.000801
6. 3×10^4
7. 3.9×10^8

---

8. 1.7×10^{-3}
9. 5×10^{-14}
10. -32
11. $-\dfrac{1}{5}$
12. $\dfrac{1}{81}$
13. 1
14. x^{-4}
15. x^{-45}
16. x^8
17. x^{-2}
18. $>$
19. $<$
20. $=$
21. $<$
22. $243x^5$
23. $-y^{12}$
24. $\dfrac{x^2}{y^{12}}$
25. 7.2×10^{18}
26. 1.5×10^4
27. 4×10^5
28. 5.12×10^{14}
29. $>$
30. $=$
31. $<$
32. $>$
33. 20
34. 9
35. 6
36. 4
37. 2.8×10^9 and 3.6×10^7
38. Approximately 78.
39.

x	0	1	2	3
y	10	5	2.5	1.25

40.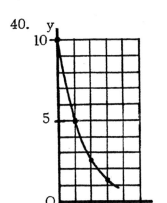

Extra Credit.

One million inches is approximately 16 miles; so it would take several hours.

Test 9A

1. 44
2. 441
3. 4
4. 10,201
5. Not possible.
6. $5x^5$
7. $25x^6$
8. $-10x^3$
9. $-5x^4$
10. $-250x^3$
11.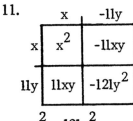

$x^2 - 121y^2$

12.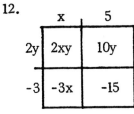

$2xy - 3x + 10y - 15$

---

13. $5x^2 + 20x$
14. $5x^2 + 21x + 4$
15. $x^2 + x - 72$
16. $9x^2 - 12x + 4$
17. $x^2 - 49$
18. $x^{10} + 2x^6 + x^2$
19. $x - 7y$
20. $x^2 - 9x + 1$
21. $x^3 + 27$
22. $x^2 + 7x - 8$
23. $8x^6$
24. $4x^{12}$
25. $10x + 4$
26. $4x^2 - x - 3$
27. $16x$
28. 9
29. $3x^2 + x - 10$
30. $3x^2 - x - 14$
31. $3x^3 + 6x^2 - 12x - 24$
32. $3x - 6$

Extra Credit.

$x^5 + 5x^4 + 10x^3 + 10x^2 + 5x + 1$

Test 9B

1. 36
2. 2,500
3. 0
4. 27
5. $4x^6$
6. Not possible.
7. $-8x^3$
8. $16x^6$
9. $-128x^3$
10. $-4x^4$

11.

	x	9y
x	x^2	$9xy$
-9y	$-9xy$	$-81y^2$

$$x^2 - 81y^2$$

12.

	2x	3
y	$2xy$	$3y$
-4	$-8x$	-12

$$2xy - 8x + 3y - 12$$

13. $7x^2 + 21x$
14. $7x^2 + 22x + 3$
15. $x^2 + 3x - 54$
16. $25x^2 - 10x + 1$
17. $x^2 - 16$
18. $x^4 + 2x^3 + x^2$
19. $3x - 2y$
20. $x^2 - 10x + 5$
21. $x^3 + 64$
22. $x^2 + 8x - 4$
23. $20x^3$
24. $25x^6$
25. $10x + 2$
26. $4x^2 + 7x - 2$
27. $22x$
28. 4
29. $12x^2 + 2x - 2$
30. $12x^2 - 2x - 4$
31. $24x^3 + 12x^2 - 6x - 3$
32. $6x - 3$

Extra Credit.
$x^4 + 12x^3 + 54x^2 + 108x + 81$

Test 9C

1. 7
2. 2,128
3. 9
4. 9,801
5. $9x^{10}$
6. $-6x^5$
7. $-3x^6$
8. $-486x^5$
9. Not possible.
10. $6x^4$
11.

	8x	y
8x	$64x^2$	$8xy$
-y	$-8xy$	$-y^2$

$$64x^2 - y^2$$

12.

	x	-4
3y	$3xy$	$-12y$
2	$2x$	-8

$$3xy + 2x - 12y - 8$$

13. $4x^2 + 24x$
14. $4x^2 + 25x + 6$
15. $x^2 + x - 56$
16. $x^2 - 9$
17. $4x^2 - 20x + 25$
18. $x^8 + 2x^5 + x^2$
19. $8x - 4y$
20. $x^2 - 8x + 7$
21. $x^3 + 8$
22. $x^2 + 4x - 18$
23. $12x^5$
24. $9x^{10}$
25. $12x - 2$
26. $5x^2 + 3x - 2$

27. $18x$
28. 16
29. $2x^2 + x - 15$
30. $2x^2 - x - 21$
31. $2x^3 + 6x^2 - 18x - 54$
32. $2x - 6$

Extra Credit.
$x^4 + 20x^3 + 150x^2 + 500x + 625$

Test 9D

1. 12
2. 9
3. 8
4. 1,331
5. $-10x^4$
6. $25x^8$
7. $1,250x^4$
8. $-5x^5$
9. $7x^3$
10. Not possible.
11.

	12x	-y
12x	$144x^2$	$-12xy$
y	$12xy$	$-y^2$

$$144x^2 - y^2$$

12.

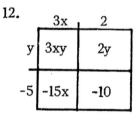

	3x	2
y	$3xy$	$2y$
-5	$-15x$	-10

$$3xy - 15x + 2y - 10$$

13. $9x^2 + 18x$
14. $9x^2 + 19x + 2$
15. $x^2 + 2x - 63$
16. $x^2 - 25$
17. $16x^2 - 8x + 1$

18. $x^6 + 2x^4 + x^2$
19. $6x - 3y$
20. $x^2 - 4x + 2$
21. $x^3 + 125$
22. $x^2 + 9x - 8$
23. $24x^4$
24. $36x^8$
25. $12x - 4$
26. $5x^2 - 14x - 3$
27. $14x$
28. 36
29. $18x^2 + 3x - 1$
30. $18x^2 - 3x - 3$
31. $54x^3 + 18x^2 - 6x - 2$
32. $6x - 2$

Extra Credit.
$x^5 + 10x^4 + 40x^3 + 80x^2 + 80x + 32$

Test 10A

1. $2^3 \cdot 3 \cdot 7$
2. $5^2 \cdot 19$
3. $11 \cdot 47$
4. $2^4 \cdot 13^4$
5. 46
6. 2
7. 6^2 (or 36)
8. 1
9. $1, x, x^2, x^3, x^4$
10. $1, 3, 7, 21, x, 3x, 7x, 21x$
11. $4x$
12. x^8
13. 9
14. xy
15. 9
16. $60x$
17. $3x^6$

18 Answers

18. $x^5 + 1$
19. $x - 6$
20. $2x + 9$
21. $16x - 3$
22. $3(4x - 7)$
23. $x(1 + 8x)$
24. $(x + 5)(x - 5)$
25. $(x + 2)(x + 19)$
26. $9x^2(x - 10)$
27. $(5x + 6)^2$
28. $(x + 4)(x - 9)$
29. $(2x + 7)(x + 6)$
30. $3(x - 1)^2$
31. $2x(x^2 + 9)$
32. $x(x + 8)(x - 8)$
33. $(x + 7y)(x - y)$
34. $(x + 5)(y - 2)$
35. $x(y + 1)(y - 1)$
Extra Credit.
$(x + 3)(x^2 - 3x + 9)$

Test 10B

1. $2 \cdot 3 \cdot 7^2$
2. $5^2 \cdot 13$
3. $11 \cdot 73$
4. $3^3 \cdot 13^3$
5. 34
6. 3
7. 1
8. 5^3 (or 125)
9. $1, x, x^2, x^3$
10. 1, 2, 11, 22, x, 2x, 11x, 22x
11. $3x$
12. x^9
13. 5
14. x^2
15. 4
16. $56x$

17. $4x^6$
18. $x^4 - 1$
19. $x - 7$
20. $5x + 8$
21. $18x - 5$
22. $7(2x - 3)$
23. $(x + 6)(x - 6)$
24. $x(1 + 5x)$
25. $(x + 3)(x + 17)$
26. $(4x - 7)^2$
27. $25x^2(x - 4)$
28. $3(x - 2)^2$
29. $(x + 5)(x - 9)$
30. $(2x + 3)(x + 9)$
31. $x(x + 4)(x - 4)$
32. $5x(x^2 + 4)$
33. $(x + 5y)(x - y)$
34. $x(y + 1)^2$
35. $(x + 2)(y - 3)$
Extra Credit.
$(x + 4)(x^2 - 4x + 16)$

Test 10C

1. $2^2 \cdot 3 \cdot 13$
2. $5^2 \cdot 17$
3. $11 \cdot 53$
4. $3^3 \cdot 7^3$
5. 26
6. 5
7. 7^3 (or 343)
8. 1
9. 1, 5, 7, 35, x, 5x, 7x, 35x
10. $1, x, x^2, x^3, x^4$
11. $2x$
12. x^6
13. 8
14. y^2
15. 1

16. $48x$
17. $2x^5$
18. $x^3 - 1$
19. $x - 9$
20. $3x + 7$
21. $12x - 5$
22. $2(6x + 11)$
23. $x(1 - 4x)$
24. $(x + 8)(x - 8)$
25. $(x + 5)(x + 13)$
26. $16x^2(x - 5)$
27. $(2x - 9)^2$
28. $x(x + 6)(x - 6)$
29. $(x + 3)(x - 12)$
30. $(2x + 5)(x + 8)$
31. $5(x - 1)^2$
32. $3x(x^2 + 4)$
33. $(x - 2y)(x + y)$
34. $y(x + 1)(x - 1)$
35. $(x + 3)(y - 5)$
Extra Credit.
$(x - 3)(x^2 + 3x + 9)$

Test 10D

1. $2 \cdot 3^2 \cdot 7$
2. $5^2 \cdot 23$
3. $11 \cdot 67$
4. $5^4 \cdot 7^4$
5. 38
6. 7
7. 1
8. 4^2 (or 16)
9. 1, 2, 13, 26, x, 2x, 13x, 26x
10. $1, x, x^2, x^3$
11. $5x$
12. x^{10}
13. 7
14. $2y$

15. 1
16. $80x$
17. $2x^4$
18. $x^2 + 1$
19. $x - 12$
20. $4x + 5$
21. $14x - 3$
22. $3(5x + 8)$
23. $(x + 9)(x - 9)$
24. $x(1 - 6x)$
25. $(x + 7)(x + 11)$
26. $(3x + 5)^2$
27. $4x^2(x - 16)$
28. $(x + 3)(x - 8)$
29. $2(x - 3)^2$
30. $7x(x^2 + 1)$
31. $(2x + 9)(x + 5)$
32. $x(x + 10)(x - 10)$
33. $(x - 3y)(x + y)$
34. $(x + 7)(y - 2)$
35. $y(x + 1)^2$
Extra Credit.
$(x - 4)(x^2 + 4x + 16)$

Test 11A

1. $\dfrac{3}{10}$
2. $\dfrac{7}{10}$
3. 1
4. True.
5. Not true.
6. Not true.
7. True.
8. -7
9. 0 and 4
10. $\dfrac{x^5}{6}$
11. Not possible.

12. $\dfrac{5}{x + y}$

13. -1

14. $\dfrac{132}{145}$

15. $\dfrac{4}{x}$

16. $\dfrac{x - 6}{6}$

17. $\dfrac{2x + x^2}{2}$

18. $\dfrac{x^2 + 25}{x + 5}$

19. $\dfrac{x}{x - 4} - \dfrac{8}{x - 4}$

20. $2 + \dfrac{x^2}{x + 1}$

21. $\dfrac{3}{2x^2}$

22. $-\dfrac{x}{2}$

23. $\dfrac{x^2 + 6x + 9}{6x}$

24. $2x^2$

25. $\dfrac{x + 8}{8x}$

26. $\dfrac{x + 5}{2}$

27. $\dfrac{x - 1}{4x}$

28. $\dfrac{9x + 6}{3x + 1}$

Extra Credit.

1. - and ·.

2. [Any equation of the form

$$\dfrac{1}{x} \text{ |||| } \dfrac{1}{x + 1} = \dfrac{1}{x(x + 1)} .]$$

Test 11B

1. $\dfrac{2}{5}$

2. $\dfrac{3}{5}$

20   Answers

---

3. 1

4. True.

5. Not true.

6. True.

7. Not true.

8. -2

9. 0 and 5

10. $\dfrac{x^6}{7}$

11. $\dfrac{x - 3y}{x + 3y}$

12. $\dfrac{4}{x - y}$

13. Not possible.

14. $\dfrac{133}{144}$

15. $\dfrac{3}{x}$

16. $\dfrac{x - 8}{8}$

17. $\dfrac{3x - x^3}{3}$

18. $\dfrac{x^2 + 4}{x - 2}$

19. $\dfrac{x}{x - 5} - \dfrac{10}{x - 5}$

20. $3 + \dfrac{x^2}{x + 1}$

21. $\dfrac{2x^2}{3}$

22. $-\dfrac{2}{x}$

23. $\dfrac{x^2 + 10x + 25}{10x}$

24. $3x^3$

25. $\dfrac{x + 12}{12x}$

26. $\dfrac{x + 7}{2}$

27. $\dfrac{x + 1}{5x}$

28. $\dfrac{16x + 8}{4x + 1}$

Extra Credit.

1. - and ·.

2. [Any equation of the form

$$\dfrac{1}{x} \text{ |||| } \dfrac{1}{x + 1} = \dfrac{1}{x(x + 1)} .]$$

Test 11C

1. $\dfrac{2}{9}$

2. $\dfrac{7}{9}$

3. 1

4. Not true.

5. True.

6. True.

7. Not true.

8. 7

9. 0 and -3

10. $\dfrac{5}{x^4}$

11. $\dfrac{x + 2y}{x - 2y}$

12. $\dfrac{x + y}{3}$

13. Not possible.

14. $\dfrac{134}{143}$

15. $\dfrac{5}{x}$

16. $\dfrac{x + 6}{6}$

17. $\dfrac{2x - x^2}{2}$

18. $\dfrac{x^2 + 16}{x - 4}$

19. $\dfrac{x}{x - 6} - \dfrac{12}{x - 6}$

20. $4 + \dfrac{x^2}{x + 1}$

21. $\dfrac{2x^6}{5}$

Extra Credit.

1. - and ·.

2. [Any equation of the form

$$\dfrac{1}{x} \text{ |||| } \dfrac{1}{x + 1} = \dfrac{1}{x(x + 1)} .]$$

22. $-\dfrac{x}{3}$

23. $\dfrac{x^2 + 12x + 36}{12x}$

24. $3x^2$

25. $\dfrac{x + 10}{10x}$

26. $\dfrac{x + 6}{2}$

27. $\dfrac{x - 1}{25}$

28. $\dfrac{4x + 4}{2x + 1}$

Extra Credit.

1. - and ·.

2. [Any equation of the form

$$\dfrac{1}{x} \text{ |||| } \dfrac{1}{x + 1} = \dfrac{1}{x(x + 1)} .]$$

Test 11D

1. $\dfrac{4}{9}$

2. $\dfrac{5}{9}$

3. 1

4. Not true.

5. True.

6. Not true.

7. True.

8. 2

9. 0 and -5

10. $\dfrac{4}{x^3}$

11. Not possible.

12. $\dfrac{x - y}{6}$

13. -1

14. $\dfrac{135}{142}$

15. $\dfrac{2}{x}$

16. $\dfrac{x + 8}{8}$

17. $\dfrac{3x + x^3}{3}$

18. $\dfrac{x^2 + 36}{x + 6}$

19. $\dfrac{x}{x - 3} - \dfrac{6}{x - 3}$

20. $5 + \dfrac{x^2}{x + 1}$

21. $\dfrac{5}{2x^6}$

22. $-\dfrac{3}{x}$

23. $\dfrac{x^2 + 8x + 16}{8x}$

24. $2x^3$

25. $\dfrac{x + 6}{6x}$

26. $\dfrac{x + 4}{2}$

27. $\dfrac{x + 1}{16}$

28. $\dfrac{25x + 10}{5x + 1}$

Extra Credit.

1. - and ·.

2. [Any equation of the form

$$\dfrac{1}{x} \ \text{\textbardbl} \ \dfrac{1}{x + 1} = \dfrac{1}{x(x + 1)} .]$$

Test 12A

1. 9 and -9
2. None.
3. 30
4. 18
5. 544
6. <
7. =
8. $5\sqrt{3}$
9. $10\sqrt{7}$

10. $12\sqrt{x}$
11. x^{72}
12. $x^2\sqrt{5x}$
13. $\dfrac{\sqrt{6}}{8}$
14. $\dfrac{\sqrt{7x}}{x}$
15. $8\sqrt{2}$
16. $\sqrt{3x}$
17. Not possible.
18. $10 + 2\sqrt{5}$
19. $35 + 3\sqrt{7}$
20. 147
21. $11 + 2\sqrt{10}$
22. $17 - 2\sqrt{30}$
23. $3\sqrt{5}$
24. x^6
25. $4\sqrt{x} - x$
26. $16 + 7\sqrt{6}$
27. $x - 9$
28. $\dfrac{5}{2}$
29. $4\sqrt{3}$
30. $2\sqrt{10} + 2$
31. $3\sqrt{5}$
32. 45
33. 220
34. 100
35. No solution.

Extra Credit.

$$\dfrac{25}{4}$$

Test 12B

1. 12 and -12
2. None.
3. 20
4. 4
5. 2,496

6. >
7. =
8. $10\sqrt{3}$
9. $3\sqrt{5}$
10. x^{50}
11. $10\sqrt{x}$
12. $x\sqrt{5x}$
13. $\dfrac{\sqrt{10}}{6}$
14. $\dfrac{\sqrt{6x}}{x}$
15. $4\sqrt{3}$
16. Not possible.
17. $\sqrt{6x}$
18. $4 + 2\sqrt{2}$
19. $50 + 3\sqrt{10}$
20. 75
21. $7 + 2\sqrt{6}$
22. $13 - 2\sqrt{22}$
23. $7\sqrt{2}$
24. x^8
25. $x - 9\sqrt{x}$
26. $x - 16$
27. $11 + 5\sqrt{5}$
28. $\dfrac{6}{5}$
29. $5\sqrt{3}$
30. $3\sqrt{7} + 3$
31. $6\sqrt{2}$
32. 72
33. 142
34. 100
35. No solution.

Extra Credit.

$$\dfrac{1}{4}$$

Test 12C

1. 10 and -10
2. None.
3. 80
4. 64
5. 1,476
6. =
7. >
8. $3\sqrt{11}$
9. $10\sqrt{5}$
10. $8\sqrt{x}$
11. x^{32}
12. $x\sqrt{3x}$
13. $\dfrac{\sqrt{2}}{12}$
14. $\dfrac{\sqrt{3x}}{x}$
15. Not possible.
16. $4\sqrt{5}$
17. $\sqrt{2x}$
18. $14 + 2\sqrt{7}$
19. $15 + 3\sqrt{3}$
20. 98
21. $6 + 2\sqrt{5}$
22. $17 - 2\sqrt{42}$
23. $2\sqrt{15}$
24. x^7
25. $16\sqrt{x} - x$
26. $x - 25$
27. $11 + 6\sqrt{3}$
28. $\dfrac{5}{3}$
29. $3\sqrt{6}$
30. $4\sqrt{5} + 4$
31. $5\sqrt{3}$
32. 75
33. 222

34. 144

35. 3

Extra Credit.

$$\frac{49}{4}$$

Test 12D

1. 3 and -3
2. None.
3. 40
4. 16
5. 2,436
6. =
7. <
8. $10\sqrt{6}$
9. $2\sqrt{11}$
10. x^{18}
11. $6\sqrt{x}$
12. $x^2\sqrt{3x}$
13. $\frac{\sqrt{14}}{10}$
14. $\frac{\sqrt{2x}}{x}$
15. Not possible.
16. $4\sqrt{6}$
17. $\sqrt{7x}$
18. $6 + 2\sqrt{3}$
19. $10 + 3\sqrt{2}$
20. 242
21. $8 + 2\sqrt{7}$
22. $16 - 2\sqrt{39}$
23. $5\sqrt{2}$
24. x^9
25. $x - 25\sqrt{x}$
26. $13 + 5\sqrt{7}$
27. $x - 1$
28. $\frac{5}{4}$
29. $3\sqrt{5}$

30. $2\sqrt{6} + 2$
31. $2\sqrt{6}$
32. 24
33. 138
34. 36
35. 4

Extra Credit.

$$\frac{9}{4}$$

Test 13A

1. $5x^4 + x^3 - 1 = 0$; quartic; 4.
2. $3x - 14 = 0$; linear; 1.
3. Yes.
4. No.
5. $x^3 + x^2 - 16x + 4 = 0$
6. Three.
7. Approximately -4.6, 0.3, and 3.4.
8.

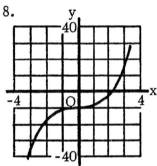

9. Approximately 2.2.
10. To be solved by the factoring method.
$\frac{1}{2}$ and -3
11. To be solved by the factoring method.
4 and 7
12. To be solved by the square-root method.
$5\sqrt{2}$ and $-5\sqrt{2}$

13. To be solved by the square-root method.
$\frac{1}{2}$ and -1
14. To be solved by completing the square.
$3 + \sqrt{10}$ and $3 - \sqrt{10}$
15. -8; no solutions.
16. 76; two solutions.
17. To be solved by the quadratic formula.
2 and $-\frac{1}{4}$
18. To be solved by the quadratic formula.
$4 + \sqrt{5}$ and $4 - \sqrt{5}$
19. 0, -3, and 2
20. $\sqrt{5}$ and $-\sqrt{5}$

Extra Credit.
$x^2 - 2x - 4 = 0$

Test 13B

1. $8x^5 - x^2 + 1 = 0$; quintic; 5.
2. $x^3 - 9x = 0$; cubic; 3.
3. Yes.
4. No.
5. $x^3 + x^2 - 16x - 20 = 0$
6. Three.
7. Approximately -3.8, -1.3, and 4.1.
8.

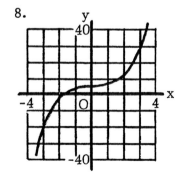

9. Approximately -1.7.
10. To be solved by the factoring method.
$\frac{1}{3}$ and -5
11. To be solved by the factoring method.
2 and 11
12. To be solved by the square-root method.
$4\sqrt{3}$ and $-4\sqrt{3}$
13. To be solved by the square-root method.
$\frac{3}{5}$ and -1
14. To be solved by completing the square.
$4 + \sqrt{7}$ and $4 - \sqrt{7}$
15. 1; two solutions.
16. 0; one solution.
17. To be solved by the quadratic formula.
$\frac{5}{2}$ and -3
18. To be solved by the quadratic formula.
$2 + \sqrt{3}$ and $2 - \sqrt{3}$
19. 0, 6, and -1
20. $\sqrt{3}$ and $-\sqrt{3}$

Extra Credit.
$x^2 - 2x - 6 = 0$

Test 13C

1. $7x^3 + x^2 - 2 = 0$; cubic; 3.
2. $x^4 + 4x^3 + x = 0$; quartic; 4.
3. No.
4. Yes.
5. $x^3 + x^2 - 16x - 6 = 0$

6. Three.

7. Approximately -4.4, -0.4, and 3.7.

8.
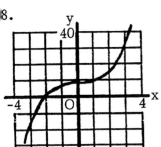

9. Approximately -2.1.

10. To be solved by the factoring method.
$\frac{1}{5}$ and -2

11. To be solved by the factoring method.
3 and 6

12. To be solved by the square-root method.
$3\sqrt{5}$ and $-3\sqrt{5}$

13. To be solved by the square-root method.
2 and $-\frac{4}{3}$

14. To be solved by completing the square.
$5 + \sqrt{11}$ and $5 - \sqrt{11}$

15. 0; one solution.

16. 41; two solutions.

17. To be solved by the quadratic formula.
$\frac{1}{3}$ and -2

18. To be solved by the quadratic formula.
$1 + \sqrt{6}$ and $1 - \sqrt{6}$

19. 0, -2, and 5

20. $\sqrt{6}$ and $-\sqrt{6}$

Extra Credit.
$$x^2 - 2x - 2 = 0$$

Test 13D

1. $6x^2 - x + 2 = 0$; quadratic; 2.

2. $x^5 + x^3 + 3x^2 = 0$; quintic; 5.

3. No.

4. Yes.

5. $x^3 + x^2 - 16x + 10 = 0$

6. Three.

7. Approximately -4.8, 0.7, and 3.1.

8.
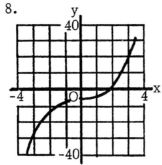

9. Approximately 1.8.

10. To be solved by the factoring method.
$-\frac{1}{3}$ and 2

11. To be solved by the factoring method.
5 and 9

12. To be solved by the square-root method.
$2\sqrt{6}$ and $-2\sqrt{6}$

13. To be solved by the square-root method.
2 and $-\frac{3}{2}$

14. To be solved by completing the square.
$2 + \sqrt{6}$ and $2 - \sqrt{6}$

15. 13; two solutions.

16. -7; no solutions.

17. To be solved by the quadratic formula.
$\frac{1}{2}$ and -5

18. To be solved by the quadratic formula.
$5 + \sqrt{2}$ and $5 - \sqrt{2}$

19. 0, -5, and 3

20. $\sqrt{2}$ and $-\sqrt{2}$

Extra Credit.
$$x^2 - 2x - 5 = 0$$

Test 14A

1. True.

2. False.

3. True.

4. False.

5. False.

6. 0.1875

7. $0.3\overline{518}$

8. $\frac{8}{33}$

9. $\frac{6}{25}$

10. $\frac{19}{18}$

11. Not possible.

12. $-\frac{1}{5}$

13. $\frac{29}{2}$

14. 0.49, $0.\overline{49}$, $0.4\overline{9}$

15. -2

16. 5 and -5

17. 3

18. None.

19. >

20. <

21. >

22. =

23. 9π

24. 7π

25. $\frac{6}{\pi}$

26. $3\sqrt{5}$

27. 50 centimeters.

28. 85 square inches.

29. 5^0 and $\sqrt[3]{8}$

30. -3

31. 0.1, $\frac{1}{4}$, and $0.\overline{6}$

32. $\sqrt{2}$ and 7π

33. Yes.

34. No; (example of two even counting numbers whose quotient is not an even counting number).

35. Yes.

36. No; (example of two even counting numbers whose difference is not an even counting number).

37. $-\frac{4}{11}$; rational.

38. $3\sqrt{7}$; irrational.

39. $\frac{3}{4}$ and $-\frac{3}{4}$; rational.

40. $6 - 2\sqrt{5}$; irrational.

Extra Credit.

1. 0.010204081632

2. If the digits are paired off from the decimal point, each successive two-digit number formed is twice the one before it.

Test 14B

1. False.
2. True.
3. False.
4. True.
5. True.
6. 0.325
7. $0.2\overline{567}$
8. $\frac{12}{25}$
9. $\frac{16}{33}$
10. $\frac{91}{30}$
11. $-\frac{1}{4}$
12. Not possible.
13. $\frac{28}{5}$
14. 0.37, $0.\overline{37}$, $0.3\overline{7}$
15. -4
16. 3 and -3
17. -2
18. 0
19. >
20. >
21. =
22. <
23. 11π
24. 3π
25. $\frac{3}{\pi}$
26. $2\sqrt{7}$
27. 88 centimeters.
28. 117 square inches.
29. $\sqrt{4}$ and 6
30. -1 and 0^3
31. $0.\overline{2}$, 0.5, and $\frac{1}{8}$
32. $\sqrt[3]{7}$

33. Yes.
34. No; (example of two odd integers whose sum is not an odd integer).
35. No; (example of two odd integers whose quotient is not an odd integer).
36. Yes.
37. $-\frac{5}{6}$; rational.
38. $6\sqrt{2}$; irrational.
39. $\frac{4}{3}$ and $-\frac{4}{3}$; rational.
40. $4 - 2\sqrt{3}$; irrational.

Extra Credit.

1. 0.0102040816 32
2. If the digits are paired off from the decimal point, each successive two-digit number formed is twice the one before it.

Test 14C

1. True.
2. True.
3. False.
4. False.
5. True.
6. 0.5625
7. $0.3\overline{148}$
8. $\frac{8}{11}$
9. $\frac{18}{25}$
10. $\frac{2}{45}$
11. $-\frac{1}{3}$
12. Not possible.

13. $\frac{41}{5}$
14. 0.58, $0.\overline{58}$, $0.5\overline{8}$
15. -3
16. 4 and -4
17. 0
18. 1 and -1
19. <
20. =
21. <
22. >
23. 7π
24. 6π
25. $\frac{10}{\pi}$
26. $2\sqrt{13}$
27. 75 centimeters.
28. 158 square inches.
29. $\sqrt[3]{1}$
30. -2 and 0^7
31. 0.3, $\frac{1}{6}$, and $0.\overline{8}$
32. 4π and $\sqrt{5}$
33. No; (example of two negative integers whose difference is not a negative integer.)
34. Yes.
35. No; (example of two negative integers whose product is not a negative integer.)
36. Yes.
37. $-\frac{7}{9}$; rational.
38. $4\sqrt{5}$; irrational.
39. $\frac{5}{2}$ and $-\frac{5}{2}$; rational.
40. $7 - 2\sqrt{6}$; irrational.

Extra Credit.

1. 0.0102040816 32
2. If the digits are paired off from the decimal point, each successive two-digit number formed is twice the one before it.

Test 14D

1. False.
2. False.
3. True.
4. True.
5. False.
6. 0.275
7. $0.1\overline{756}$
8. $\frac{9}{25}$
9. $\frac{4}{11}$
10. $\frac{49}{45}$
11. $-\frac{1}{6}$
12. $\frac{21}{4}$
13. Not possible.
14. 0.28, $0.\overline{28}$, $0.2\overline{8}$
15. -5
16. None.
17. 2
18. 1
19. =
20. >
21. <
22. <
23. 13π
24. 2π
25. $\frac{9}{\pi}$
26. $2\sqrt{10}$
27. 82 centimeters.
28. 66 square inches.

29. 1^0 and $\sqrt{9}$

30. -6

31. $0.\overline{5}$, $\frac{1}{7}$, and 0.8

32. 2π and $\sqrt[3]{4}$

33. No; (example of two positive integers whose difference is not a positive integer.)

34. Yes.

35. Yes.

36. No; (example of two positive integers whose quotient is not a positive integer.)

37. $-\frac{3}{7}$; rational.

38. $4\sqrt{6}$; irrational.

39. $\frac{2}{5}$ and $-\frac{2}{5}$; rational.

40. $8 - 2\sqrt{7}$; irrational.

Extra Credit.

1. 0.0102040816 32

2. If the digits are paired off from the decimal point, each successive two-digit number formed is twice the one before it.

Test 15A

1. $\frac{2}{3}$

2. $\frac{15}{8}$

3. $\frac{3x^2}{5}$

4. $\frac{4}{7}$

5. $9 + 2x$

6. $4x - 5$

7. $-\frac{2}{3}$

8. $4\sqrt{3}$ and $-4\sqrt{3}$

9. $-\frac{1}{5}$ and 1

10. $9\frac{3}{4}$

11. -8

12. True for all numbers except 4.

13. $-1 + \sqrt{11}$ and $-1 - \sqrt{11}$

14. 18 miles per hour.

15. $r = \frac{2v}{3}$

16. 20

17. $a + ab$

18. $\frac{a + b}{b}$

19. $\sqrt{a^2 - 1}$ and $-\sqrt{a^2 - 1}$

20. $\frac{b}{a + 1}$

Extra Credit.

$1\frac{1}{3}$ hours.

Test 15B

1. $\frac{1}{2}$

2. $\frac{9}{5}$

3. $\frac{3}{5x^2}$

4. $\frac{2}{9}$

5. $3x + 5$

6. $2 - 8x$

7. $-\frac{3}{2}$

8. $2\sqrt{11}$ and $-2\sqrt{11}$

9. $-\frac{1}{7}$ and 1

10. $12\frac{4}{5}$

11. $-\frac{5}{2}$

12. True for all numbers except 3.

13. $2 + \sqrt{14}$ and $2 - \sqrt{14}$

14. 12 miles per hour.

15. $r = \frac{2v}{3}$

16. 14

17. $a - ab$

18. $\frac{a - b}{b}$

19. $\sqrt{1 - a^2}$ and $-\sqrt{1 - a^2}$

20. $\frac{b}{a - 1}$

Extra Credit.

$\frac{30}{31}$ hour.

Test 15C

1. $\frac{2}{5}$

2. $\frac{19}{10}$

3. $\frac{2x^5}{7}$

4. $\frac{3}{5}$

5. $2 - 6x$

6. $7x + 3$

7. $-\frac{4}{3}$

8. $3\sqrt{5}$ and $-3\sqrt{5}$

9. $\frac{1}{3}$ and -1

10. $14\frac{1}{4}$

11. $-\frac{3}{2}$

12. True for all numbers except 2.

13. $1 + \sqrt{7}$ and $1 - \sqrt{7}$

14. 15 miles per hour.

15. $r = \frac{2v}{3}$

16. 18

17. $ab + b$

18. $\frac{a + b}{a}$

19. $\sqrt{b^2 - 1}$ and $-\sqrt{b^2 - 1}$

20. $\frac{a}{b + 1}$

Extra Credit.

$1\frac{13}{47}$ hours.

Test 15D

1. $\frac{1}{3}$

2. $\frac{11}{6}$

3. $\frac{2}{7x^5}$

4. $\frac{5}{8}$

5. $6x - 3$

6. $4 + 5x$

7. $-\frac{3}{4}$

8. $2\sqrt{10}$ and $-2\sqrt{10}$

9. $\frac{1}{4}$ and -1

10. $11\frac{1}{5}$

11. $-3\frac{1}{2}$

12. True for all numbers except 5.

13. $1 + \sqrt{13}$ and $1 - \sqrt{13}$

14. 9 miles per hour.

15. $r = \dfrac{2v}{3}$

16. 16

17. $b - ab$

18. $\dfrac{a - b}{a}$

19. $\sqrt{1 - b^2}$ and $-\sqrt{1 - b^2}$

20. $\dfrac{a}{b - 1}$

Extra Credit.

$1\dfrac{1}{19}$ hours.

Test 16A

1. $=$
2. $>$
3. $<$
4. $<$
5. $=$
6. $x \leq 7$
7. $-4 < x < 1$
8. None.
9. $<$
10. $\geq$
11. None.
12. $<$
13. $>$
14. None.
15. Yes.
16. No.
17. Yes.
18. No.
19. No.
20. Yes.
21. $x > 35$
22. $x < -6$
23. $x \leq -5$
24. $x > 18$

25. $x \geq \dfrac{6}{5}$
26. $x < -\dfrac{3}{2}$
27. $x < 24$
28. $x < \dfrac{b}{a}$
29. $x < \dfrac{ac}{b}$
30. $x \leq \dfrac{1}{b - a}$
31. 16 and -4
32. $-3 + x$ and $-3 - x$

33. ◄——○————○——►
        -3   3

34. ◄——●—|—●——►
         4 6 8

35. ◄——●—|—●——►
      -8 -2   4

36. 2 and -2
37. 2 and -8
38. 7 and -7
39. $x > 11$ or $x < -11$
40. No solutions.

Extra Credit.
-1 and 5

Test 16B

1. $>$
2. $=$
3. $>$
4. $=$
5. $<$
6. $x > 3$
7. $-2 \leq x \leq 7$
8. $<$
9. None.
10. None.
11. $\geq$
12. $>$
13. None.

14. $=$
15. Yes.
16. Yes.
17. No.
18. Yes.
19. No.
20. No.
21. $x < 24$
22. $x > -7$
23. $x \geq -3$
24. $x < 60$
25. $x \leq \dfrac{4}{3}$
26. $x < -\dfrac{15}{2}$
27. $x > 21$
28. $x > \dfrac{1 - b}{a}$
29. $x > \dfrac{a}{b}$
30. $x \geq \dfrac{b}{a - c}$
31. 17 and -7
32. $-2 + x$ and $-2 - x$

33. ◄——○————○——►
        -7   7

34. ◄——●—|———●——►
        -4 2   8

35. ◄——●—|—●——►
      -8 -6 -4

36. 6 and -6
37. 8 and -8
38. 8 and 2
39. $x > 2$ or $x < -2$
40. True for all numbers.

Extra Credit.
-2 and 4

Test 16C

1. $>$
2. $<$
3. $>$
4. $<$
5. $=$
6. $x < -2$
7. $3 \leq x \leq 10$
8. None.
9. $=$
10. None.
11. $>$
12. $=$
13. $<$
14. $>$
15. No.
16. Yes.
17. Yes.
18. No.
19. Yes.
20. No.
21. $x < 30$
22. $x > -4$
23. $x \geq -9$
24. $x < 24$
25. $x \leq \dfrac{5}{4}$
26. $x < -\dfrac{7}{3}$
27. $x > 14$
28. $x > \dfrac{1 + b}{a}$
29. $x > \dfrac{ab}{c}$
30. $x \geq \dfrac{c}{a - b}$
31. 19 and -11
32. $-8 + x$ and $-8 - x$

3.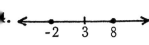
   -1   1
4.
   -2 3 8
5.
   -8 -5 -2
6. 9 and -9
7. 7 and -7
8. 7 and -11
9. True for all numbers.
10. -16 < x < 16
Extra Credit.
   -2 and 6

Test 16D

1. <
2. =
3. <
4. >
5. =
6. $x \geq -4$
7. -1 < x < 6
8. $\geq$
9. None.
10. <
11. None.
12. >
13. <
14. None.
15. Yes.
16. No.
17. No.
18. No.
19. Yes.
20. Yes.
21. x > 20
22. x < -9
23. $x \leq -2$
24. x > 35

25. $x \geq \dfrac{3}{2}$
26. $x < -\dfrac{20}{3}$
27. x < 15
28. $x < \dfrac{-b}{a}$
29. $x < \dfrac{ab}{c}$
30. $x \leq \dfrac{1}{a - b}$
31. 20 and -6
32. -4 + x and -4 - x
33.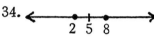
   -2   2
34.
   2 5 8
35.
   -8 -3 2
36. 5 and -5
37. 5 and 1
38. 8 and -8
39. No solutions.
40. x > 4 or x < -14
Extra Credit.
   -3 and 5

Test 17A

1. Geometric; common ratio, 7.
2. Arithmetic; common difference, -3.
3. Neither.
4. 59
5. -324
6. 25
7. $\sqrt{29}$
8. 20
9. 12
10. 8, 32, 128, 512
11. 2, 32, 162, 512

12. 8, 11, 14, 17
13. 14, 7, 0, -7
14. $0, 1\frac{1}{2}, 2\frac{2}{3}, 3\frac{3}{4}$
15. 8, 11, 14, 17 and 14, 7, 0, -7
16. 8, 32, 128, 512
17. $t_n = n - 5$
18. 95
19. $t_n = 4^n$
20. 4,096
21. $t_n = -3n$
22. -75
23. $t_n = \dfrac{8}{n}$
24. $\dfrac{1}{3}$
25. 5,940
26. 405
27. d = 12 + 0.50(n - 1)
28. $26.50
29.

n	0	1	2	3
p	17	34	68	136

30. $p = 17 \cdot 2^n$
Extra Credit.
   114 feet.

Test 17B

1. Neither.
2. Arithmetic; common difference, -1.5.
3. Geometric; common ratio, 6.
4. -1,280
5. 54
6. 16
7. $\dfrac{5}{6}$
8. 39
9. 15
10. 2, 16, 54, 128

11. 6, 18, 54, 162
12. 7, 2, -3, -8
13. $\dfrac{1}{2}, \dfrac{2}{3}, \dfrac{3}{4}, \dfrac{4}{5}$
14. 21, 24, 27, 30
15. 7, 2, -3, -8 and 21, 24, 27, 30
16. 6, 18, 54, 162
17. $t_n = -2n$
18. -30
19. $t_n = \dfrac{n}{10}$
20. 4
21. $t_n = n - 4$
22. 96
23. $t_n = \sqrt{n + 1}$
24. 9
25. 4,760
26. 2,500
27. d = 15 + 0.50(n - 1)
28. $29.50
29.

n	0	1	2	3
p	14	28	56	112

30. $p = 14 \cdot 2^n$
Extra Credit.
   34 feet.

Test 17C

1. Arithmetic; common difference, 4.
2. Neither.
3. Geometric; common ratio, $\dfrac{1}{2}$.
4. -1,875
5. 20
6. 58
7. 625
8. 25
9. 15
10. 12, 14, 16, 18

11. 4, 1, -2, -5

12. 4, 32, 108, 256

13. 12, 36, 108, 324

14. $2, \dfrac{3}{2}, \dfrac{4}{3}, \dfrac{5}{4}$

15. 12, 14, 16, 18 and 4, 1, -2, -5

16. 12, 36, 108, 324

17. $t_n = \dfrac{n}{4}$

18. 15

19. $t_n = n + 8$

20. 108

21. $t_n = 2^n$

22. 128

23. $t_n = -5n$

24. -150

25. 8,320

26. 512

27. $d = 18 + 0.25(n - 1)$

28. $25.25

29. n 0 1 2 3
    p 13 26 52 104

30. $p = 13 \cdot 2^n$

Extra Credit.
   54 feet.

Test 17D

1. Neither.

2. Geometric; common ratio, 8.

3. Arithmetic; common difference, 3.5.

4. 67

5. -5

6. 22

7. 125

8. 17

9. 8

10. 4, 2, 0, -2

11. 3, 48, 243, 768

12. 12, 48, 192, 768

13. 10, 15, 20, 25

14. $0, \dfrac{1}{2}, \dfrac{2}{3}, \dfrac{3}{4}$

15. 4, 2, 0, -2 and 10, 15, 20, 25

16. 12, 48, 192, 768

17. $t_n = \sqrt{n}$

18. 10

19. $t_n = -4n$

20. -80

21. $t_n = \dfrac{3}{n}$

22. $\dfrac{1}{5}$

23. $t_n = n + 6$

24. 46

25. 5,460

26. 256

27. $d = 20 + 0.25(n - 1)$

28. $27.25

29. n 0 1 2 3
    p 18 36 72 144

30. $p = 18 \cdot 2^n$

Extra Credit.
   24 feet.

Midyear A

1. d
2. a
3. b
4. e
5. c
6. d
7. a
8. e
9. d
10. b
11. c
12. a
13. d
14. c
15. c
16. c
17. d
18. a
19. e
20. (a)
21. c
22. b
23. a
24. d
25. b
26. a
27. e
28. d
29. c
30. d
31. b
32. e
33. a
34. a
35. b
36. e
37. c
38. e
39. d
40. (b)
41. a
42. c
43. e
44. e
45. a
46. e
47. d
48. b
49. d
50. d
51. c
52. a

53. b
54. c
55. e
56. d
57. b
58. c
59. a
60. (c)
61. b
62. c
63. c
64. a
65. d
66. c
67. b
68. a
69. c
70. b
71. c
72. e
73. a
74. e
75. a
76. d
77. b
78. d
79. b
80. (d)

The graphs for problems 20, 40, 60, and 80 are shown on the next page.

Midyear B

1. c
2. b
3. a
4. d
5. b
6. a

7. e
8. d
9. c
10. d
11. b
12. e
13. a
14. a
15. b
16. e
17. c
18. e
19. d
20. (b)
21. b
22. c
23. c
24. a
25. d
26. c
27. b
28. a
29. c
30. b
31. c

Graphs for problems 20, 40, 60, and 80 of forms A, B, C, and D.

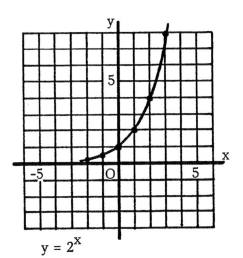

$y = 2^x$

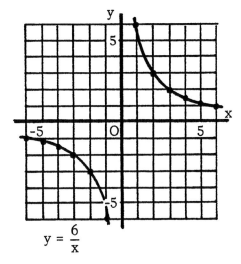

$y = \dfrac{6}{x}$

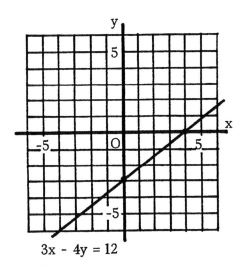

$3x - 4y = 12$

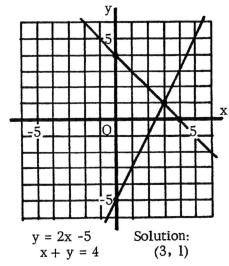

$y = 2x - 5$ Solution:
$x + y = 4$ (3, 1)

32. e	46. d	60. (a)	74. c
33. a	47. a	61. a	75. e
34. e	48. e	62. c	76. d
35. a	49. d	63. e	77. b
36. d	50. b	64. e	78. c
37. b	51. c	65. a	79. a
38. d	52. a	66. e	80. (c)
39. b	53. d	67. d	
40. (d)	54. c	68. b	The graphs for problems 20, 40, 60, and 80 are shown above.
41. d	55. c	69. d	
42. a	56. c	70. d	
43. b	57. d	71. c	
44. e	58. a	72. a	
45. c	59. e	73. b	

Answers 29

Midyear C

1. a
2. c
3. e
4. e
5. a
6. e
7. d
8. b
9. d
10. d
11. c
12. a
13. b
14. c
15. e
16. d
17. b
18. c
19. a
20. (c)
21. d
22. a
23. b
24. e
25. c
26. d
27. a
28. e
29. d
30. b
31. c
32. a
33. d
34. c
35. c
36. c
37. d

38. a
39. e
40. (a)
41. b
42. c
43. c
44. a
45. d
46. c
47. b
48. a
49. c
50. b
51. c
52. e
53. a
54. e
55. a
56. d
57. b
58. d
59. b
60. (d)
61. c
62. b
63. a
64. d
65. b
66. a
67. e
68. d
69. c
70. d
71. b
72. e
73. a
74. a
75. b
76. e

77. c
78. e
79. d
80. (b)

The graphs for problems 20, 40, 60, and 80 are shown on the previous page.

Midyear D

1. b
2. c
3. c
4. a
5. d
6. c
7. b
8. a
9. c
10. b
11. c
12. e
13. a
14. e
15. a
16. d
17. b
18. d
19. b
20. (d)
21. a
22. c
23. e
24. e
25. a
26. e
27. d
28. b
29. d
30. d

31. c
32. a
33. b
34. c
35. e
36. d
37. b
38. c
39. a
40. (c)
41. c
42. b
43. a
44. d
45. b
46. a
47. e
48. d
49. c
50. d
51. b
52. e
53. a
54. a
55. b
56. e
57. c
58. e
59. d
60. (b)
61. d
62. a
63. b
64. e
65. c
66. d
67. a
68. e
69. d

70. b

71. c

72. a

73. d

74. c

75. c

76. c

77. d

78. a

79. e

80. (a)

The graphs for problems 20, 40, 60, and 80 are shown on page 29 of this Answer Section.

Final A

1. a

2. b

3. a

4. b

5. b

6. c

7. d

8. e

9. b

10. e

11. c

12. b

13. d

14. c

15. c

16. d

17. d

18. c

19. a

20. c

21. a

22. a

23. b

24. d

25. c

26. d

27. e

28. a

29. d

30. e

31. d

32. d

33. c

34. b

35. b

36. b

37. e

38. e

39. d

40. d

41. c

42. c

43. a

44. b

45. d

46. c

47. b

48. b

49. c

50. e

51. c

52. d

53. c

54. a

55. b

56. d

57. d

58. b

59. d

60. b

61. a

62. c

63. d

64. d

65. c

66. c

67. b

68. e

69. c

70. d

71. c

72. b

73. b

74. d

75. e

76. b

77. d

78. d

79. e

80. a

Final B

1. a

2. a

3. b

4. d

5. c

6. d

7. e

8. a

9. d

10. e

11. d

12. d

13. c

14. b

15. b

16. b

17. e

18. e

19. d

20. d

21. a

22. c

23. d

24. d

25. c

26. c

27. b

28. e

29. c

30. d

31. c

32. b

33. b

34. d

35. e

36. b

37. d

38. d

39. e

40. a

41. a

42. b

43. a

44. b

45. b

46. c

47. d

48. e

49. b

50. e

51. c

52. b

53. d

54. c

55. c

56. d

57. d

58. c

59. a
60. c
61. c
62. c
63. a
64. b
65. d
66. c
67. b
68. b
69. c
70. e
71. c
72. d
73. c
74. a
75. b
76. d
77. d
78. b
79. d
80. b

Final C

1. c
2. c
3. a
4. b
5. d
6. c
7. b
8. b
9. c
10. e
11. c
12. d
13. c
14. a
15. b

16. d
17. d
18. b
19. d
20. b
21. a
22. b
23. a
24. b
25. b
26. c
27. d
28. e
29. b
30. e
31. c
32. b
33. d
34. c
35. c
36. d
37. d
38. c
39. a
40. c
41. a
42. c
43. d
44. d
45. c
46. c
47. b
48. e
49. c
50. d
51. c
52. b
53. b
54. d

55. e
56. b
57. d
58. d
59. e
60. a
61. a
62. a
63. b
64. d
65. c
66. d
67. e
68. a
69. d
70. e
71. d
72. d
73. c
74. b
75. b
76. b
77. e
78. e
79. d
80. d

Final D

1. a
2. c
3. d
4. d
5. c
6. c
7. b
8. e
9. c
10. d
11. c

12. b
13. b
14. d
15. e
16. b
17. d
18. d
19. e
20. a
21. c
22. c
23. a
24. b
25. d
26. c
27. b
28. b
29. c
30. e
31. c
32. d
33. c
34. a
35. b
36. d
37. d
38. b
39. d
40. b
41. a
42. a
43. b
44. d
45. c
46. d
47. e
48. a
49. d
50. e

51. d
52. d
53. c
54. b
55. b
56. b
57. e
58. e
59. d
60. d
61. a
62. b
63. a
64. b
65. b
66. c
67. d
68. e
69. b
70. e
71. c
72. b
73. d
74. c
75. c
76. d
77. d
78. c
79. a
80. c

Word Problems, Set 1

1. 7 cents to the first, 14 cents to the second, 21 cents to the third, and 28 cents to the fourth
2. 8 years old
3. Apple, 1 cent; pear, 2 cents; orange, 6 cents
4. 20

5. 40 cents and 27 cents
6. 9
7. A is 84, B is 42, and C is 14
8. 14
9. 23 dollars
10. 20

Word Problems, Set 2

1. Horse, $32; chaise, $128; house, $640
2. 20
3. 4
4. 8
5. Men, 54; women, 18; children, 9
6. 12
7. A, 3,427; B, 2,878; C, 3,865
8. 2, 4, 6, 8, 10, and 12
9. 27 miles
10. $275

Word Problems, Set 3

1. A, 30; B, 10
2. Boots, $6; shoes, $2
3. John, 24; William, 8
4. 25 gallons of wine at 9 shillings and 75 gallons of wine at 13 shillings
5. 60
6. The cover, 20 ounces; the second cup, 16 ounces
7. Men, 6 shillings each; boys, 4 shillings each
8. A, $40; B, $20
9. Orange, 5 cents; apple, 4 cents
10. First horse, $90; second horse, $60
11. Sherry, $12 a dozen; port, $10 a dozen
12. 8

Word Problems, Set 4

1. 11
2. 9 and 16
3. Length, 18 feet; breadth, 6 feet
4. 320
5. $8
6. 3 yards
7. 8,910

Word Problems, Set 5

1. 39
2. $24
3. 24 feet
4. $135
5. 90
6. $2,800
7. $120
8. 96
9. $15 and $35
10. 54
11. A, 5; B, 6
12. 47

Exercises on Fundamental Operations

1. 1,066
2. 1,492
3. 3.123
4. 3.141
5. 2,001
6. 10,000
7. 0.003
8. 238
9. 1
10. 0.1331
11. 1
12. 0
13. y
14. 0
15. 0
16. 7
17. Cannot divide by zero.
18. 6
19. 0
20. 3
21. 30
22. 6
23. 2
24. 63
25. 111
26. 13,640
27. 2
28. 0
29. 10
30. 4
31. 44
32. 2
33. 4
34. 0
35. 2
36. 12
37. Not possible.
38. 2
39. 2
40. Not possible.
41. 2
42. 4
43. 0
44. 10
45. 90
46. 0
47. 0
48. 0
49. 26
50. 0
51. 26

Exercises on the Integers

1. (Figure omitted.)
2. (Figure omitted.)
3. -3
4. -2
5. 0
6. -11
7. 10^3
8. 10^2
9. -1
10. $(-2)^3$
11. -3^2
12. $(-1)^3$
13. x
14. y - 2
15. (Figure omitted.)
16. 10
17. -2
18. 0
19. -1
20. 29
21. 0
22. 7
23. 8
24. 1
25. -17
26. -6
27. 3
28. 5
29. 9
30. -1
31. 2
32. 2
33. 0
34. -135
35. 0

Exercises on Equations in One Variable: Area, Perimeter, and Rate

1. 30
2. 1
3. 9
4. 6
5. 6
6. 3
7. 40
8. 12
9. 27
10. 100
11. 3
12. 3
13. $-\dfrac{9}{5}$
14. 2
15. $\dfrac{4}{3}$
16. $\dfrac{7}{3}$
17. 4
18. 19
19. 1
20. $\dfrac{2}{3}$
21. 0
22. 10
23. 17
24. -40
25. -5
26. 1
27. 2
28. 0
29. 5
30. 8.4
31. Perimeter, 6x; area, $2x^2$.
32. Perimeter, 12x + 2; area, $9x^2 + 3x$.
33. Perimeter, 6x + 4; area, $2x^2 + 4x$.
34. $\dfrac{1}{8}$
35. 24
36. $\dfrac{1}{8}$ mile per minute.

Exercises on Formulas, Equations and Problems Having More than One Variable

1. x = y - 7
2. $V = \dfrac{600}{P}$
3. $x = \dfrac{1}{yz}$
4. $x = \dfrac{1 - y}{1 + y}$
5. $y = \dfrac{1 - x}{x}$

6. $F = \dfrac{9C + 160}{5}$

7. $C = \dfrac{5F - 160}{9}$

8. $y = 2 - 2x$

9. $x = \dfrac{4 - 2y}{4}$

10. $x = -y$

11. $a = \dfrac{32}{t^2}$

12. $t^2 = \dfrac{32}{a}$

13. $y = -x + 1$; slope, -1; y-intercept, 1.

14. $y = 4x + 3$; slope, 4; y-intercept, 3.

15. $y = -x + 2$; slope, -1; y-intercept, 2.

16. $y = -\dfrac{2}{3}x + 2$; slope, $-\dfrac{2}{3}$; y-intercept, 2.

17. $y = 6x - 6$; slope, 6; y-intercept, -6.

18. $y = x + 2$; slope, 1; y-intercept, 2.

19. $y = x + 1$; slope, 1; y-intercept, 1.

20. $y = x + 1$; slope, 1; y-intercept, 1.

21. Equations 13 and 15 are inconsistent; equations 18 and 19 (and 18 and 20) are inconsistent; equations 19 and 20 are equivalent.

22. $(-11, 14)$

23. $(0, 0)$

24. $(8, 2)$

25. Inconsistent.

26. $(1, 3)$

27. $(7, 5)$

28. $(2, -1)$

29. $(-3, 2)$

30. Equivalent.

31. $(\dfrac{3}{2}, \dfrac{3}{2})$

32. $(4, 2)$

33. $(-3, 5)$

34. $(6, 6)$

35. $(-2, 3)$

36. Equivalent.

37. $(-3, -1)$

38. $(1, 7)$

39. $(-1, 2)$

40. $(1, -4)$

41. Inconsistent.

42.-46. (The graphs are omitted.)

47. $2.80.

48. $2.30.

49. 20 miles.

50. 7 miles per hour.

Exercises on Polynomials

1. 5, 2, 1, 2, 5

2. -6, 0, 0, 0, 6

3. -13, -2, 1, 2, 7

4. 0, 0, 0, 0, 0

5. -9, -5, -1, 9, 31

6. $3x^3 + 2x^2 - 4$

7. $3x^2 + 4x - 10$

8. $-x^3 + x^2 + 2$

9. $3x^3 - x + 1$

10. $-2x^2 + 5x - 3$

11. $x^3 + x^2 + x - 1$

12. $y^2 - 4$

13. $2x^3 + x^2 - x - 1$

14. $-5y + 9$

15. $-2x^2 + 10x - 7$

16. $x^5 + x^4 - x^3 - x^2 - 4x + 2$

17. $x^3 + x - 3$

18. $4z^3 + 2z^2 + 5$

19. $11x + 9$

20. $3z^2 - 11z - 10$

21. $4x^2 - 12x + 9$

22. $z - 2z^2 + z^3$

23. $9 - 4x^2$

24. $x^3 - x^2 + x - 1$

25. $16 - z^4$

26. $x^3 - x^2 - x + 1$

27. $-6y^2 + 11y + 10$

28. $z^3 - 3z^2 + 2z + 6$

29. $15x^3 - 29x^2 - 14x$

30. $0.02x^2 + 0.5x - 3$

31. $4x^2 + 2x - 12$

32. $4x^2$

33. $2x - 3$

34. $6x - 4$

35. $3x - 5$

36. $16x^2 + 12x + 9$

37. $x - 3$

38. $x^3 - 2x + 6$

39. $x^5 + x^4 + x^3 + x^2 + x + 1$

Exercises on Factoring

1. $2 \cdot 5^2 \cdot 11$

2. $2^3 \cdot 3^2 \cdot 5 \cdot 13$

3. $3 \cdot 5 \cdot 7 \cdot 13$

4. $2^4 \cdot 5^4$

5. $2^3 \cdot 3 \cdot 5^2 \cdot 17$

6. $2^5 \cdot 5 \cdot 41$

7. $(x - 2)(2x - 1)$

8. $(4x + 5)(4x - 5)$

9. $3z(x - 3)(2x - 1)$

10. $4z(4z - 1)$

11. $(5x - 1)(x + 2)$

12. $x(4w^2 + 1)$

13. $3(2x + 3)^2$

14. $(x^2 + 4)(x + 2) \cdot (x - 2)$

15. $(ax - 3)^2$

16. $(3x + 2)(4x + 3)$

17. $(5x - 1)^2$

18. $5x(5x - 2)$

19. $(3x - 2)(4x - 3)$

20. $yz(z + y)$

21. $3z^2(3z - 2)(3z + 2)$

22. $2(x + 6)(y - 3)$

23. $2x^3(x + 6)(x - 5)$

24. $w^2(5x + 2)(x - 1)$

25. $2(x - 6)(3x + 14)$

26. $3z(3 + z)(3 - z)$

27. $4(3 - y)(4 - 3y)$

28. $z^2(5x + 6)(3x - 5)$

29. $(w - 2)^2(w + 2)^2$

30. $30(x + 2)(x - 2)$

31. $(x + y)(x - 1)$

32. $2y^2(3y + 1)(y - 3)$

33. $2x(3y - 2)^2$

34. $y(6y - 1)(y + 6)$

35. $(x + 6)(z - 1)$

36. $(x - y)(y - z)$

Exercises on Fractions

1. $\dfrac{2}{9}$

2. $\dfrac{64}{11}$

3. $\dfrac{x}{2a}$

4. -3

5. $\dfrac{-x}{a + x}$

6. $\dfrac{1}{2y + x}$

7. $\dfrac{(x + y)^2}{x^2 + y^2}$

8. $\dfrac{xy - 1}{4xy + 1}$

9. $\dfrac{1}{(2x - 3)(3x + 2)}$

10. 1

11. 1

12. $\dfrac{1}{3}$

13. 3

14. $-\dfrac{7}{15}$

15. 3.05

16. $1\dfrac{13}{15}$

17. $-\dfrac{6}{5}$ or $-1\dfrac{1}{5}$

18. $\dfrac{x + 5}{x^2}$

19. $\dfrac{3y + 2x - x^2 y}{xy}$

20. $\dfrac{2}{1 - x^2}$

21. -1

22. $\dfrac{1}{x}$

23. $\dfrac{2x - 1}{1 - x}$

24. $\dfrac{x^2 + y^2}{x - y}$

25. $\dfrac{7x}{(x - 3)(x + 3)(2x - 1)}$

26. $\dfrac{3}{7}$

27. $\dfrac{5ax}{y^2}$

28. $\dfrac{3x^2}{10a^2 y}$

29. $\dfrac{1 - y}{7}$

30. $\dfrac{x}{3}$

31. $\dfrac{1}{(y + 1)(x + 1)}$

32. $\dfrac{x(x + 2)}{(2x - 5)(x + 3)}$

33. $\dfrac{(x + 1)(x - 2)}{x^2}$

34. $\dfrac{(y - 4)(y - 1)}{(y + 1)(y + 3)}$

35. $\dfrac{x + 1}{x}$

36. 2

37. $\dfrac{27x}{x^2 + 1}$

38. $\dfrac{xy(x - 1)}{a^3}$

39. $\dfrac{2(y^2 + 2y + 4)(2y - 1)}{y}$

40. $\dfrac{x^3}{y^3}$

41. $\dfrac{x}{y}$

42. $\dfrac{5}{3}$ or $1\dfrac{2}{3}$

43. $\dfrac{x + 1}{x - 1}$

44. $\dfrac{x}{x + 1}$

45. $\dfrac{x^2}{x - 2}$

46. $\dfrac{x - 1}{x}$

47. $\dfrac{2x + 2}{x + 2}$

48. $\dfrac{1}{x}$

49. $\dfrac{x^6 - 1}{x^2}$

50. $\dfrac{x^2 + y^2}{x^2 - y^2}$

Exercises on Quadratic Equations

1. 3 and 5

2. 2 and -2

3. 0 and 4

4. $\dfrac{4}{3}$ and $-\dfrac{4}{3}$

5. 3 and -3

6. -3

7. -2 and -3

8. 2 and -5

9. $-\dfrac{1}{3}$

10. $\dfrac{1}{2}$ and -2

11. $-\dfrac{1}{2}$ and 2

12. 8 and -2

13. 16 and -1

14. 1 and $-\dfrac{1}{2}$

15. $-\dfrac{2}{3}$ and $-\dfrac{3}{2}$

16. $\dfrac{1 \pm \sqrt{5}}{2}$

17. $\dfrac{3 \pm \sqrt{5}}{2}$

18. 1 and 3

19. $\dfrac{-5 \pm \sqrt{5}}{2}$

20. $1 \pm \sqrt{2}$

21. -1 and $-\dfrac{1}{3}$

22. $\dfrac{1}{2}$ and $-\dfrac{1}{3}$

23. $\dfrac{-3 \pm \sqrt{13}}{2}$

24. $\dfrac{2}{3}$ and 1

25. 5 and -3

26. -1 and $-\dfrac{3}{4}$

27. 0 and $\dfrac{1}{2}$

28. $\dfrac{4}{5}$ and $-\dfrac{4}{5}$

29. $\dfrac{\sqrt{5} \pm 1}{2}$

30. 1

31. a) (Figure omitted.)
    b) 32
    c) Two.
    d) 0 and 6

32. a) (Figure omitted.)
    b) 0
    c) One.
    d) 3

33. a) (Figure omitted.)
    b) -12
    c) None.
    d) No solutions.

34. 9

35. 10

36. 4

37. -1 and $-\dfrac{1}{3}$

38. 1 and 9

39. $\dfrac{-2 \pm \sqrt{3}}{5}$

40. 8 and 10

41. 0, 1, and 2

42. -1

43. 2, 3, and -3

44. 0, 5, and $\dfrac{2}{3}$

45. 2 and -2

22. 1

23. -1 and $-\dfrac{8}{3}$

24. No solutions.

25. a) $\dfrac{5}{5-x} + \dfrac{5}{5+x}$

    b) $\dfrac{5\sqrt{2}}{2}$ kilometers per hour.

Exercises on Fractional Equations

1. $\dfrac{5}{2}$

2. 2

3. $\dfrac{1}{2}$

4. 1

5. -3

6. 3 and 7

7. $\dfrac{1}{2}$ and -3

8. $-\dfrac{1}{2}$

9. 5 and $\dfrac{8}{3}$

10. 2 and 4

11. 1 and -1

12. No solutions.

13. 1

14. $\dfrac{1}{2}$

15. 5 and -6

16. 2

17. No solutions.

18. 11 and -9

19. -8 and 7

20. $\dfrac{2}{3}$ and -1

21. 0